O for a book and a shady nook,
Either indoors or out;
With the green leaves whispering overhead,
Or the street cries all about.
Where I may read all at my ease
Both of the new and old;
For a jolly good book whereon to look
Is better to me than gold.

John Wilson, London bookseller

Grandfather's Chair

True Stories
from
New England History
1620-1803

by Nathaniel Hawthorne

EDGEWATER BOOKS
BUHL • IDAHO

It takes a great deal of history to produce a little literature.

Henry James in *Life of Nathaniel Hawthorne*

Edgewater Books publishes vivid histories and classic works for the young and old. This unabridged version may reflect both the richness of virtues and the poverty of prejudices common to the people and the times in which it was written. Each Edgewater Brief Edition is carefully annotated, handsomely formatted, durably bound, and printed on quality paper.

Published by Edgewater Books
www.edgewater-books.com
P.O. Box 643
Buhl, Idaho 83316 USA

ISBN-13: 978-0-9792968-0-2
ISBN-10: 0-9792968-0-3

Table of Contents

(A '†' or '‡' next to a word in a chapter indicates a reference to it in the Edgewater Brief at the back of this book.)

Edgewater Essay
for Parents and Teachers
The Best History Instruction

Liberally adapted from *Special Method in History* by Charles A. McMurry, PhD.

Without dropping a plummet into the depths of our subject at the moment of opening, we may at least all agree that it's good for our children to gain an intelligent interest in the families and people of their neighborhood, in the health and comfort of the people of their own town, in the personal history of well-known characters, such as Longfellow, Lincoln, John Winthrop, Martin Luther King, and Mahatma Gandhi, and in larger matters of public concern.

This intelligent interest is awakened first of all by a lifelike picture of the personal fortunes of men like Daniel Boone, or George Washington Carver, or King David, or Alfred the Great. Such biographies give insight into the struggles, dangers and triumphs of and to individuals, communities and nations. The life stories of inventors like Stephenson, Fulton, and Cooper, and benefactors like Florence Nightingale, John Eliot, and William Penn, kindle social sympathies of lasting worth. Children, having strong personal interests and affections, can quickly interpret the lives of individuals. They tacitly compare themselves with such persons, and are stimulated to like feelings and actions. Suitable biographies disclose to children the broad arena of possible action and at the same time give an impulse to the full extent of their own best powers. The lives of the world's chiefs are often called the very substance of history, as in Emerson's *Representative Men*. They serve as examples and ideals to arouse enthusiasms, and have an inestimable power in giving the initial impulses for the formation of character in children.

Through reading of history, interest may be awakened in the common life of people, as in old-fashioned customs and modes of dress, in the style and peculiarity of their houses, furniture, and domestic arrangements, in their hardships and sufferings caused by war, pestilence, or drought, in their toils in the field, forest, or shop, on lakes and rivers, in their homes and family life, in their churches and religious ideas, in their games and amusements, in their schools, jury trials, and prisons, in their social, educational, and political gatherings, and in the peculiarities of different cultures in our own and other countries.

We shall get a better view of the aim and educative value of history by an inquiry into the question: How far can the children relive the past and reproduce in themselves the helpful experience of men? In thought, feeling, and imagination, to what extent may a child live over again the scenes, the dangers, the struggles, the disasters, and the triumphs of previous generations? For example, the long labors and the final landing of Columbus in America, the life of the Pilgrims at Plymouth, the voyage of Magellan, the struggles of the pioneers, the horrors of the slave trade, the scenes in camps, in cabinets, in senates, or on the battlefield? If history can be taught in such a way that a child may take up into himself the experiences of history, that all he has read and studied shall become a part of his real self, that the experiences of men in different countries may ripen into the wisdom of youth approaching maturity, we shall see that history may be a powerful educator, indeed.

It has been often observed that history is a moral study. It deals with subject matter which illustrates moral ideas and obligations. It teaches morals concretely both in individuals and in communities or states. Froude, in his essay on history, says: "First, it is a voice forever sounding across the centuries the laws of right and wrong. Opinions alter, manners change, creeds rise and fall, but the moral law is written on the tablets of eternity. For every false word or unrighteous deed, for cruelty and oppression, for lust or vanity, the price has to be paid at last; not always by the chief offenders, but paid by someone."

For this reason history should never be studied in a dry, matter-of-fact, formal way. The people of history should live before the thought of the child as vividly as the hero of the tale. The imagination must reconstruct the pictures of the past. Quoting Froude again: "We learn in it to sympathize with what is great and good; we learn to hate what is base."

The teacher is not left without resources when asked to teach morals through history. The historical materials most suitable for children are prolific in striking examples of higher conduct. If these illustrations of action are placed clearly before the children in their true colors, they will carry their own moral. They make their own appeal to the child's sympathy and moral judgment.

History should also be taught that it may contribute largely to the better understanding of many topics in literature, geography, and natural science. Without the background and general setting of history much of the best literature based upon history cannot be understood and appreciated. One needs to get a framework of Scottish history and geography in order to understand Scott's "Marmion", "Lady of the Lake," and "The Lay of the Last Minstrel." Many of Webster's great speeches can only be understood in the light of history, and this statement may be made also of many of the best poems, ballads, novels, orations, and essays in our literature. History supplies, therefore, much of the concrete material and broader survey of historical events which constitute a basis for understanding some of the best literature of the world. This gives us an organic or vital relation between these great studies.

In summing up the aim of history instruction we may say that it should be so taught that children may become thoroughly and intelligently interested in individuals and in the concerns of society. History is preeminently a moral study and moral practice. To give a vivid and intense realization of social duties and obligations is the essence of the best history instruction.

Author's Preface

In writing this ponderous tome, the author's desire has been to describe the eminent characters and remarkable events of our annals, in such a form and style that the young might make acquaintance with them of their own accord. For this purpose, while ostensibly relating the adventures of a Chair, he has endeavored to keep a distinct and unbroken thread of authentic history. The Chair is made to pass from one to another of those personages, of whom he thought it most desirable for the young reader to have vivid and familiar ideas, and whose lives and actions would best enable him to give picturesque sketches of the times. On its sturdy oaken legs, it trudges diligently from one scene to another, and seems always to thrust itself in the way, with most benign complacency, whenever a historical personage happens to be looking round for a seat.

There is certainly no method, by which the shadowy outlines of departed men and women can he made to assume the hues of life more effectually, than by connecting their images with the substantial and homely reality of a fireside chair. It causes us to feel at once that these characters of history had a private and familiar existence, and were not wholly contained within that cold array of outward action, which we are compelled to receive as the adequate representation of their lives. If this impression can be given, much is accomplished.

Setting aside Grandfather and his auditors, and excepting the adventures of the Chair, which form the machinery of the work, nothing in the ensuing pages can be termed fictitious. The author, it is true, has sometimes assumed the license of filling up the outline of history with details, for which he has none but imaginative authority, but which, he hopes, do not violate nor give a false coloring to the truth. He believes that, in this respect, his narrative will not be found to convey ideas and impressions, of which the reader may hereafter find it necessary to purge his mind.

The author's great doubt is, whether he has succeeded in writing a book which will be readable by the class for whom he intends it. To make a lively and entertaining narrative for children, with such unmalleable material as is presented by the sombre, stern, and rigid characteristics of the Puritans and their descendants, is quite as difficult an attempt, as to manufacture delicate playthings out of the granite rocks on which New England is founded.

Part One

1620-1692
True Stories from New England

The First Epoch of Grandfather's Chair

Chapter I
Grandfather and the Children and the Chair

Grandfather had been sitting in his old armchair, all that pleasant afternoon, while the children were pursuing their various sports, far off or near at hand. Sometimes you would have said, "Grandfather is asleep;" but still, even when his eyes were closed, his thoughts were with the young people, playing among the flowers and shrubbery of the garden.

He heard the voice of Laurence, who had taken possession of a heap of decayed branches which the gardener had lopped from the fruit trees, and was building a little hut for his cousin Clara and himself. He heard Clara's gladsome voice, too, as she weeded and watered the flower bed which had been given her for her own. He could have counted every footstep that Charley took, as he trundled his wheelbarrow along the gravel walk. And though Grandfather was old and gray-haired, yet his heart leaped with joy whenever little Alice came fluttering, like a butterfly, into the room. She had made each of the children her playmate in turn, and now made Grandfather her playmate too, and thought him the merriest of them all.

At last the children grew weary of their sports; because a summer afternoon is like a long lifetime to the young.

So they came into the room together, and clustered round Grandfather's great chair. Little Alice, who was hardly five years old, took the privilege of the youngest, and climbed his knee. It was a pleasant thing to behold that fair and golden-haired child in the lap of the old man, and to think that, different as they were, the hearts of both could be gladdened with the same joys.

"Grandfather," said little Alice, laying her head back upon his arm, "I am very tired now. You must tell me a story to make me go to sleep."

"That is not what storytellers like," answered Grandfather, smiling. "They are better satisfied when they can keep their auditors† awake."

"But here are Laurence, and Charley, and I," cried cousin Clara, who was twice as old as little Alice. "We will all three keep wide awake. And pray, Grandfather, tell us a story about this strange looking old chair."

Now, the chair in which Grandfather sat was made of oak, which had grown dark with age, but had been rubbed and polished till it shone as bright as mahogany. It was very large and heavy, and had a back that rose high above Grandfather's white head. This back was curiously carved in open work, so as to represent flowers and foliage and other devices; which the children had often gazed at, but could never understand what they meant. On the very tiptop of the chair, over the head of Grandfather himself, was a likeness of a lion's head, which had such a savage grin that you would almost expect to hear it growl and snarl.

The children had seen Grandfather sitting in this chair ever since they could remember any thing. Perhaps the younger of them supposed that he and the chair had come into the world together, and that both had always been as old as they were now. At this time, however, it happened to be the fashion for ladies to adorn their drawing rooms with the oldest and oddest chairs that could be found. It seemed to cousin Clara that if these ladies could have seen Grandfather's old chair, they would have thought it worth all the rest together. She wondered if it were not even older than Grandfather himself, and longed to know all about its history.

"Do, Grandfather, talk to us about this chair," she repeated.

"Well, child," said Grandfather, patting Clara's cheek, "I can tell you a great many stories of my chair. Perhaps your cousin Laurence would like to hear them too. They would teach him something about the history and distinguished people of his country, which he has never read in any of his schoolbooks."

Cousin Laurence was a boy of twelve, a bright scholar, in whom an early thoughtfulness and sensibility† began to show themselves. His young fancy kindled at the idea of knowing all the adventures of this venerable† chair. He looked

A STATE CHAIR NOT UNLIKE GRANDFATHER'S CHAIR

eagerly in Grandfather's face; and even Charley, a bold, brisk, restless little fellow of nine, sat himself down on the carpet, and resolved to be quiet for at least ten minutes, should the story last so long.

Meantime, little Alice was already asleep; so Grandfather, being much pleased with such an attentive audience, began to talk about matters that had happened long ago.

Chapter II
The Puritans and the Lady Arbella

But, before relating the adventures of the chair, Grandfather found it necessary to speak of the circumstances that caused the first settlement of New England. For it will soon be perceived that the story of this remarkable chair cannot be told without telling a great deal of the history of the country.

So, Grandfather talked about the Puritans,† as those persons were called who thought it sinful to practise the religious forms and ceremonies which the Church of England had borrowed from the Roman Catholics. These Puritans suffered so much in England that, in 1607, many of them went over to Holland, and lived ten or twelve years at Amsterdam and Leyden. But they feared that, if they continued there much longer, they should cease to be English, and should adopt all the manners and ideas and feelings of the Dutch. For this and other reasons, in the year 1620, they embarked on board of the ship *Mayflower*, and crossed the ocean to the shores of Cape Cod. There they made a settlement, and called it Plymouth; which, though now a part of Massachusetts, was for a long time a colony by itself. And thus was formed the earliest settlement of the Puritans in America.

Meantime, those of the Puritans who remained in England continued to suffer grievous persecution on account of their religious opinions. They began to look around them for some spot where they might worship God, not as the king and bishops thought fit, but according to the dictates of their own consciences. When their brethren had gone from Holland to America, they bethought themselves that they likewise might find refuge from persecution there. Several gentlemen among them purchased a tract of country on the coast of Massachusetts Bay, and obtained a charter† from King Charles, which authorized them to make laws for the settlers. In the year 1628, they sent over a few people, with John Endicott at their head, to commence a plantation at Salem. Peter Palfrey, Roger Conant, and one or two more, had built houses there in 1626, and may be considered as the first settlers of that ancient town. Many other Puritans prepared to follow Endicott.

"And now we come to the chair, my dear children," said Grandfather. "This chair is supposed to have been made of an oak tree which grew in the park of the English earl of Lincoln, between two and three centuries ago. In its younger days it used, probably, to stand in the hall of the earl's castle. Do not you see the coat of arms of the family of Lincoln, carved in the open work of the back? But when his daughter, the Lady Arbella, was married to a certain Mr. Johnson, the earl gave her this valuable chair."

"Who was Mr. Johnson?" inquired Clara.

"He was a gentleman of great wealth, who agreed with

PURITAN SWORD, POT, AND PLATTER

the Puritans in their religious opinions," answered Grandfather. "And as his belief was the same as theirs, he resolved that he would live and die with them. Accordingly, in the month of April, 1630, he left his pleasant abode and all his comforts in England, and embarked with the Lady Arbella, on board of a ship bound for America."

As Grandfather was frequently impeded by the questions and observations of his young auditors, we deem it advisable to omit all such prattle as is not essential to the story. We have taken some pains to find out exactly what Grandfather said, and here offer to our readers, as nearly as possible in his own words, the story of

The Lady Arbella

The ship in which Mr. Johnson and his lady embarked, taking Grandfather's chair along with them, was called the *Arbella,* in honor of the lady herself. A fleet of ten or twelve vessels, with many hundred passengers, left England about the same time; for a multitude of people, who were discontented with the king's government and oppressed by the bishops, were flocking over to the new world. One of the vessels in the fleet was that same *Mayflower* which had carried the Puritan pilgrims to Plymouth. And now, my children, I would have you fancy yourselves in the cabin of the good ship *Arbella*; because if you could behold the passengers aboard that vessel, you would feel what a blessing and honor it was for New England to have such settlers. They were the best men and women of their day.

TOMB OF A MATE
OF THE MAYFLOWER

Among the passengers was John Winthrop, who had sold the estate of his forefathers, and was going to prepare a new home for his wife and children in the wilderness. He had the king's charter in his keeping, and was appointed the first Governor of Massachusetts. Imagine him a person of grave and benevolent aspect,† dressed in a black velvet suit, with a broad ruff around his neck and a peaked beard upon his chin. There was likewise a minister of the Gospel, whom the English bishops had forbidden to preach, but who knew that he should have liberty both to preach and pray in the forests of America. He wore a black cloak, called a Geneva cloak, and had a black velvet cap, fitting close to his head, as was the fashion of almost all the Puritan clergymen. In their company came Sir Richard Saltonstall, who had been one of the five first projectors of the new colony. He soon returned to his native country. But his descendants still remain in New England; and the good old family name is as much respected in our days as it was in those of Sir Richard.

Not only these, but several other men of wealth and pious ministers, were in the cabin of the *Arbella*. One had banished himself forever from the old hall where his ancestors had lived for hundreds of years. Another had left his quiet parsonage, in a country town of England. Others had come from the universities of Oxford or Cambridge, where they had gained great fame for their learning. And here they all were, tossing upon the uncertain and dangerous sea, and bound for a home that was more dangerous than even the sea itself. In the cabin, likewise, sat the Lady Arbella in her chair, with a gentle and sweet expression on her face, but looking too pale and feeble to endure the hardships of the wilderness.

Every morning and evening the Lady Arbella gave up her great chair to one of the ministers, who took his place in it and read passages from the Bible to his companions. And thus, with prayers and pious conversation, and frequent singing of hymns, which the breezes caught from their lips and scattered far over the desolate waves, they prosecuted their voyage, and sailed into the harbor of Salem in the month of June.

At that period there were but six or eight dwellings in the town; and these were miserable hovels, with roofs of straw and wooden chimneys. The passengers in the fleet either built huts with bark and branches of trees, or erected tents of cloth till they could provide themselves with better shelter. Many of them went to form a settlement at Charlestown. It was thought fit that the Lady Arbella should tarry in Salem for a time; she was probably received as a guest into the family of John Endicott. He was the chief person in the plantation, and had the only comfortable house which the newcomers had beheld since they left England. So now, children, you must imagine Grandfather's chair in the midst of a new scene.

Suppose it a hot summer's day, and the lattice-windows of a chamber in Mr. Endicott's house thrown wide open. The Lady Arbella, looking paler than she did on shipboard, is sitting in her chair, and thinking mournfully of far-off England. She rises and goes to the window. There, amid patches of garden ground and cornfield, she sees the few wretched hovels of the settlers, with the still ruder† wigwams and cloth tents of the passengers who had arrived in the same fleet with herself. Far and near stretches the dismal forest of pine trees, which throw their black shadows over the whole land, and likewise over the heart of this poor lady.

All the inhabitants of the little village are busy. One is clearing a spot on the verge of the forest for his homestead; another is hewing the trunk of a fallen pine tree, in order to build himself a dwelling; a third is hoeing in his field of Indian corn. Here comes a huntsman out of the woods, dragging a bear which he has shot, and shouting to the neighbors to lend him a hand. There goes a man to the seashore, with a spade and a bucket, to dig a mess of clams, which were a principal article of food with the first settlers. Scattered here and there are two or three dusky figures, clad in mantles of fur, with ornaments of bone hanging from their ears, and the feathers of wild birds in their coal-black hair. They have belts of shell-work slung across their shoulders, and are armed with bows and arrows and flint-headed spears. These are an Indian sagamore† and his attendants, who have come to gaze at the labors of the white men. And now rises a cry that a pack of wolves have seized a young calf in the pasture; and every man snatches up his gun or

JOHN ENDICOTT

pike,† and runs in chase of the marauding beasts.

Poor Lady Arbella watches all these sights, and feels that this new world is fit only for rough and hardy people. None should be here but those who can struggle with wild beasts and wild men, and can toil in the heat or cold, and can keep their hearts firm against all difficulties and dangers. But she is not one of these. Her gentle and timid spirit sinks within her; and turning away from the window she sits down in the great chair, and wonders whereabouts in the wilderness her friends will dig her grave.

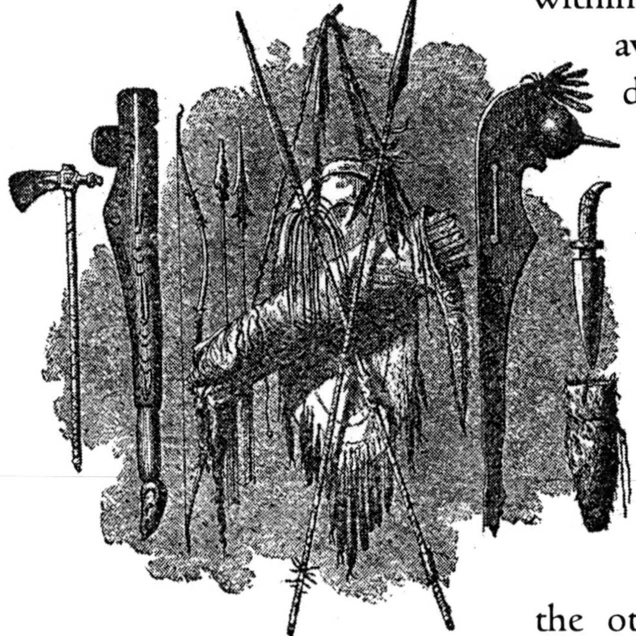

INDIAN WEAPONS

Mr. Johnson had gone, with Governor Winthrop and most of the other passengers, to Boston, where he intended to build a house for Lady Arbella and himself. Boston was then covered with wild woods, and had fewer inhabitants even than Salem. During her husband's absence, poor Lady Arbella felt herself growing ill, and was hardly able to stir from the great chair. Whenever John Endicott noticed her despondency, he doubtless addressed her with words of comfort. "Cheer up, my good lady!" he would say. "In a little time, you will love this rude life of the wilderness as I do." But Endicott's heart was as bold and resolute as iron, and he could not understand why a woman's heart should not be of iron too.

Still, however, he spoke kindly to the lady, and then hastened forth to till his cornfield and set out fruit trees, or to bargain with the Indians for furs, or perchance to oversee the building of a fort. Also being a magistrate, he had often to punish some idler or evildoer, by ordering him to be set in the stocks or scourged at the whipping post. Often, too, as was the custom of the times, he and Mr. Higginson, the minister of Salem, held long religious talks together. Thus John Endicott was a man of multifarious† business, and had no time to look back regretfully to his native land. He felt himself fit for the new world, and for the work that he had to do, and set himself resolutely to accomplish it.

What a contrast, my dear children, between this bold, rough, active man, and the gentle Lady Arbella, who was fading away, like a pale English flower, in the shadow of the forest! And now the great chair was often empty, because Lady Arbella grew too weak to arise from bed.

Meantime, her husband had pitched upon a spot for their new home. He returned from Boston to Salem, travelling through the woods on foot, and leaning on his pilgrim's staff. His heart yearned within him; for he was eager to tell his wife of the new home which he had chosen. But when he beheld her pale and hollow cheek, and found how her strength was wasted, he must have known that her appointed home was in a better land. Happy for him then,–happy both for him and her,–if they remembered that there was a path to heaven, as well from this heathen wilderness as from the Christian land whence they had come. And so, in one short month from her arrival, the gentle Lady Arbella faded away and died. They dug a grave for her in the new soil, where the roots of the pine trees impeded their spades; and when her bones had rested there nearly two hundred years, and a city had sprung up around them, a church of stone was built upon the spot.

***

Charley, almost at the commencement of the foregoing narrative, had galloped away with a prodigious clatter, upon Grandfather's stick,† and was not yet returned. So large a boy should have been ashamed to ride upon a stick. But Laurence and Clara had listened attentively, and were affected by this true story of the gentle lady, who had come so far to die so soon. Grandfather had supposed that little Alice was asleep, but, towards the close of the story, happening to look down upon her, he saw that her blue eyes were wide open, and fixed earnestly upon his face. The tears had gathered in them, like dew upon a delicate flower; but when Grandfather ceased to speak, the sunshine of her smile broke forth again.

"Oh, the lady must have been so glad to get to heaven!" exclaimed little Alice.

"Grandfather, what became of Mr. Johnson?" asked Clara.

"His heart appears to have been quite broken," answered Grandfather; "for he died at Boston within a month after the death of his wife. He was buried in the very same tract of ground, where he had intended to build a dwelling for

INDIAN WARRIORS

Lady Arbella and himself. Where their house would have stood there was his grave.

"I never heard any thing so melancholy!" said Clara.

"The people loved and respected Mr. Johnson so much," continued Grandfather, "that it was the last request of many of them, when they died, that they might be buried as near as possible to this good man's grave. And so the field became the first burial ground in Boston. When you pass through Tremont Street, along by King's Chapel, you see a burial ground, containing many old gravestones and monuments. That was Mr. Johnson's field."

"How sad is the thought," observed Clara, "that one of the first things which the settlers had to do, when they came to the new world, was to set apart a burial ground!"

"Perhaps," said Laurence, "if they had found no need of burial grounds here, they would have been glad, after a few years, to go back to England."

Grandfather looked at Laurence, to discover whether he knew how profound and true a thing he had said.

Chapter III
The Red Cross

Not long after Grandfather had told the story of his great chair, there chanced to be a rainy day. Our friend Charley, after disturbing the household with beat of drum and riotous shouts, races up and down the staircase, overturning of chairs, and much other uproar, began to feel the quiet and confinement within doors intolerable. But as the rain came down in a flood, the little fellow was hopelessly a prisoner, and now stood with sullen aspect at a window, wondering whether the sun itself were not extinguished by so much moisture in the sky.

Charley had already exhausted the less eager activity of the other children; and they had betaken themselves to occupations that did not admit of his companionship. Laurence sat in a recess† near the bookcase, reading, not for the first time, the *Midsummer Night's Dream*. Clara was making a rosary of beads for a little figure of a Sister of Charity, who was to attend the Bunker Hill Fair, and lend her aid in erecting the Monument‡. Little Alice sat on Grandfather's footstool, with a picture book in her hand; and, for every picture, the child was telling Grandfather a story. She did not read from the book, (for little Alice had not much skill in reading,) but told the story out of her own heart and mind.

Charley was too big a boy, of course, to care any thing about little Alice's stories, although Grandfather appeared to listen with a good deal of interest. Often, in a young child's ideas and fancies, there is something which it requires the thought of a lifetime to comprehend. But Charley was of opinion that if a story must be told, it had better be told by Grandfather, than little Alice.

"Grandfather, I want to hear more about your chair," said he.

Now Grandfather remembered that Charley had galloped away upon a stick, in the midst of the narrative of poor Lady Arbella, and I know not whether he would have thought it worthwhile to tell another story, merely to gratify such an inattentive auditor as Charley. But Laurence laid down his book and seconded the request. Clara drew her chair nearer to Grandfather, and little Alice immediately closed her picture book, and looked up into his face. Grandfather had not the heart to disappoint them.

He mentioned several persons who had a share in the settlement of our country, and who would be well worthy of remembrance, if we could find room to tell about them all. Among the rest, Grandfather spoke of the famous Hugh Peters, a minister of the Gospel, who did much good to the inhabitants of Salem. Mr. Peters afterwards went back to England, and was chaplain to Oliver Cromwell‡; but Grandfather did not tell the children what became of this upright and zealous man, at last. In fact, his auditors were growing impatient to hear more about the history of the chair.

"After the death of Mr. Johnson," said he, "Grandfather's

MONUMENT AT NEW PLYMOUTH TO MARK THE SITE OF THE LANDING OF THE PLYMOUTH FATHERS

chair came into the possession of Roger Williams. He was a clergyman, who arrived at Salem, and settled there in 1631. Doubtless the good man has spent many a studious hour in this old chair, either penning a sermon, or reading some abstruse† book of theology, till midnight came upon him unawares. At that period, as there were few lamps or candles to be had, people used to read or work by the light of pitchpine torches. These supplied the place of the "midnight oil," to the learned men of New England."

Grandfather went on to talk about Roger Williams, and told the children several particulars, which we have not room to repeat. One incident, however, which was connected with his life, must be related, because it will give the reader an idea of the opinions and feelings of the first settlers of New England. It was as follows:

The Red Cross

While Roger Williams sat in Grandfather's chair, at his humble residence in Salem, John Endicott would often come to visit him. As the clergy had great influence in temporal† concerns, the minister and magistrate would talk over the occurrences of the day, and consult how the people might be governed according to scriptural laws.

One thing especially troubled them both. In the old national banner of England, under which her soldiers have fought for hundreds of years, there is a red cross, which has been there ever since the days when England was in subjection to the Pope. The cross, though a holy symbol, was abhorred by the Puritans, because they considered it a relic of Popish† idolatry. Now, whenever the train-band of Salem was mustered, the soldiers, with Endicott at their head, had no other flag to march under than this same old papistical† banner of England, with the Red Cross in the midst of it. The banner of the Red Cross, likewise, was flying on the walls of the fort of Salem; and a similar one was displayed in Boston Harbor, from the fortress on Castle Island.

"I profess, brother Williams," Captain Endicott would say, after they had been talking of this matter, "it distresses a Christian man's heart, to see this idolatrous cross flying over our heads. A stranger beholding it, would think that we had undergone all our hardships and dangers, by sea and in the wilderness, only to get new dominions for the Pope of Rome."

"Truly, good Mr. Endicott," Roger Williams would answer, "you speak as an honest man and Protestant Christian should. For mine own part, were it my business to draw a sword, I should reckon it sinful to fight under such a banner. Neither can I, in my pulpit, ask the blessing of Heaven upon it."

Such, probably, was the way in which Roger Williams and John Endicott used to talk about the banner of the Red Cross. Endicott, who was a prompt and resolute man, soon determined that Massachusetts, if she could not have a banner of her own, should at least be delivered from that of the Pope of Rome.

Not long afterwards there was a military muster at Salem. Every able-bodied man, in the town and neighborhood, was there. All were well armed, with steel caps upon their heads, plates of iron upon their breasts and at their backs, and gorgets† of steel around their necks. When the sun shone upon these ranks of iron-clad men, they flashed and blazed with a splendor that bedazzled the wild Indians, who had come out of the woods to gaze at them. The soldiers had long pikes,† swords, and muskets, which were fired with matches, and were almost as heavy as a small cannon.

These men had mostly a stern and rigid aspect. To judge by their looks, you might have supposed that there was as much iron in their hearts, as there was upon their heads and

THE PURITAN AND THE SOLDIER

breasts. They were all devoted Puritans, and of the same temper as those with whom Oliver Cromwell afterwards overthrew the throne of England. They hated all the relics of Popish superstition as much as Endicott himself; and yet, over their heads, was displayed the banner of the Red

Cross.

Endicott was the captain of the company. While the soldiers were expecting his orders to begin their exercise, they saw him take the banner in one hand, holding his drawn sword in the other. Probably he addressed them in a speech, and explained how horrible a thing it was, that men, who had fled from Popish idolatry into the wilderness, should be compelled to fight under its symbols here. Perhaps he concluded his address somewhat in the following style.

"And now, fellow soldiers, you see this old banner of England. Some of you, I doubt not, may think it treason for a man to lay violent hands upon it. But whether or no it be treason to man, I have good assurance in my conscience that it is no treason to God. Wherefore I have resolved that we will rather be God's soldiers, than soldiers of the Pope of Rome; and in that mind I now cut the Papal Cross out of this banner."

And so he did. And thus, in a province belonging to the crown of England, a captain was found bold enough to deface the King's banner with his sword.

When Winthrop, and the other wise men of Massachusetts, heard of it, they were disquieted, being afraid that Endicott's act would bring great trouble upon himself and them. An account of the matter was carried to King Charles‡; but he was then so much engrossed by dissensions with his people that he had no leisure to punish the offender. In other times, it might have cost Endicott his life, and Massachusetts her charter.

***

"I should like to know, Grandfather," said Laurence, when

the story was ended, "whether, when Endicott cut the Red Cross out of the banner, he meant to imply that Massachusetts was independent of England?"

"A sense of the independence of his adopted country, must have been in that bold man's heart," answered Grandfather; "but I doubt whether he had given the matter much consideration, except in its religious bearing. However, it was a very remarkable affair, and a very strong expression of Puritan character."

Grandfather proceeded to speak further of Roger Williams, and of other persons who sat in the great chair, as will be seen in the following chapter.

Chapter IV
Eighty-two Wrong Opinions

"Roger Williams," said Grandfather, "did not keep possession of the chair a great while. His opinions of civil and religious matters differed, in many respects, from those of the rulers and clergymen of Massachusetts. Now the wise men of those days believed that the country could not be safe, unless all the inhabitants thought and felt alike."

"Does anybody believe so in our days Grandfather?" asked Laurence.

"Possibly there are some who believe it," said Grandfather; "but they have not so much power to act upon their belief, as the magistrates and ministers had, in the days of Roger Williams. They had the power to deprive this good man of his home, and to send him out from the midst of them, in search of a new place of rest. He was banished in 1634, and went first to Plymouth colony; but as the people there held the same opinions as those of Massachusetts, he was not suffered to remain among them. However, the wilderness was wide enough; so Roger Williams took his staff and travelled into the forest, and made treaties with the Indians, and began a plantation which he called Providence."

"I have been to Providence on the railroad," said Charley.

"It is but a two hours' ride."

"Yes, Charley," replied Grandfather; "but when Roger Williams travelled thither, over hills and valleys, and through the tangled woods, and across swamps and streams, it was a journey of several days. Well; his little plantation is now grown to be a populous city; and the inhabitants have a great veneration for Roger Williams. His name is familiar in the mouths of all because they see it on their bank bills. How it would have perplexed this good clergyman, if he had been told that he should give his name to the Roger Williams Bank!"‡

"When he was driven from Massachusetts," said Laurence, "and began his journey into the woods, he must have felt as if he were burying himself forever from the sight and knowledge of men. Yet the whole country has now heard of him, and will remember him forever."

"Yes," answered Grandfather, "it often happens that the outcasts of one generation are those who are reverenced as the wisest and best of men by the next. The securest fame is that which comes after a man's death. But let us return to our story. When Roger Williams was banished, he appears to have given the chair to Mrs. Anne Hutchinson. At all events it was in her possession in 1637. She was a very sharp witted and well-instructed lady, and was so conscious of her own wisdom and abilities that she thought it a pity that the world should not have the benefit of them. She therefore used to hold lectures in Boston, once or twice a week, at which most of the women attended. Mrs. Hutchinson presided at these meetings, sitting, with great state and dignity, in Grandfather's chair."

ROGER WILLIAMS IN THE FOREST

"Grandfather, was it positively this very chair?" demanded Clara, laying her hand upon its carved elbow.

"Why not, my dear Clara?" said Grandfather. "Well; Mrs. Hutchinson's lectures soon caused a great disturbance; for the ministers of Boston did not think it safe and proper that a woman should publicly instruct the people in religious doctrines. Moreover, she made the matter worse, by declaring that the Rev. Mr. Cotton was the only sincerely pious and holy clergyman in New England. Now the clergy of those days had quite as much share in the government of the country, though indirectly, as the magistrates themselves; so you may imagine what a host of powerful enemies were raised up against Mrs. Hutchinson. A synod was convened; that is to say, an assemblage of all the ministers in Massachusetts. They declared that there were eighty-two erroneous opinions on religious subjects, diffused among the people, and that Mrs. Hutchinson's opinions were of the number."

ANNE HUTCHINSON'S TRIAL

"If they had eighty-two wrong opinions," observed Charley, "I don't see how they could have any right ones."

"Mrs. Hutchinson had many zealous friends and converts," continued Grandfather. "She was favored by young Henry Vane, who had come over from England a year or two before, and had since been chosen governor of the colony, at the age of twenty-four. But Winthrop, and most of the other leading men, as well as the ministers, felt an abhorrence of her doctrines. Thus two opposite parties were formed; and so fierce were the dissensions that it was feared the consequence would be civil war and bloodshed. But Winthrop and the ministers being the most powerful, they disarmed and imprisoned Mrs. Hutchinson's adherents. She, like Roger Williams, was banished."

"Dear Grandfather, did they drive the poor woman into the woods?" exclaimed little Alice, who contrived to feel a human interest even in these discords of polemic† divinity.

"They did, my darling," replied Grandfather; "and the end of her life was so sad, you must not hear it. At her departure, it appears from the best authorities that she gave the great chair to her friend, Henry Vane. He was a young man of wonderful talents and great learning, who had imbibed the religious opinions of the Puritans, and left England with the intention of spending his life in Massachusetts. The people chose him governor; but the controversy about Mrs. Hutchinson, and other troubles, caused him to leave the country in 1637. You may read the subsequent events of his life in the *History of England*."‡

"Yes, Grandfather," cried Laurence; "and we may read them better in Mr. Upham's biography of Vane‡. And what a beautiful death he died, long afterwards! Beautiful, though it was on a scaffold."

"Many of the most beautiful deaths have been there," said Grandfather. "The enemies of a great and good man can in no other way make him so glorious, as by giving him the crown of martyrdom."

In order that the children might fully understand the all-important history of the chair, Grandfather now thought fit to speak of the progress that was made in settling several colonies. The settlement of Plymouth, in 1620, has already been mentioned. In 1635, Mr. Hooker‡ and Mr. Stone, two ministers, went on foot from Massachusetts to Connecticut, through the pathless woods, taking their whole congregation along with them. They founded the town of Hartford. In 1638, Mr. Davenport,‡ a very celebrated minister, went, with other people, and began a plantation at New Haven. In the same year, some persons who had been persecuted in Massachusetts, went to the Isle of Rhodes, since called Rhode Island, and settled there. About this time, also, many settlers had gone to Maine, and were living without any regular government. There were likewise settlers near Piscataqua River, in the region which is now called New Hampshire.

Thus, at various points along the coast of New England, there were communities of Englishmen. Though these communities were independent of one another, yet they had a common dependence upon England; and, at so vast a distance from their native home, the inhabitants must all have felt like brethren. They were fitted to become one united people, at a future period. Perhaps their feelings of brotherhood were the stronger, because different nations had formed settlements to the north and to the south. In Canada and Nova Scotia were colonies of French. On the banks of the Hudson River was a colony of Dutch, who had taken possession of that region many years before, and called it New Netherlands.

***

Grandfather, for aught I know, might have gone on to speak of Maryland and Virginia; for the good old gentleman really seemed to suppose that the whole surface of the United States was not too broad a foundation to place the four legs of his chair upon. But, happening to glance at Charley, he perceived that this naughty boy was growing impatient, and meditating another ride upon a stick. So here, for the present, Grandfather suspended the history of his chair.

Chapter V
Liberty and Privilege in New England

The children had now learned to look upon the chair with an interest, which was almost the same as if it were a conscious being, and could remember the many famous people whom it had held within its arms.

Even Charley, lawless as he was, seemed to feel that this venerable chair must not be clambered upon nor overturned, although he had no scruple in taking such liberties with every other chair in the house. Clara treated it with still greater reverence, often taking occasion to smooth its cushion, and to brush the dust from the carved flowers and grotesque figures of its oaken back and arms. Laurence would sometimes sit a whole hour, especially at twilight, gazing at the chair, and, by the spell of his imaginations, summoning up its ancient occupants to appear in it again.

Little Alice evidently employed herself in a similar way; for once, when Grandfather had gone abroad, the child was heard talking with the gentle Lady Arbella, as if she were still sitting in the chair. So sweet a child as little Alice may fitly talk with angels, such as the Lady Arbella had long since become.

Grandfather was soon importuned for more stories about

the chair. He had no difficulty in relating them; for it really seemed as if every person, noted in our early history, had, on some occasion or other, found repose within its comfortable arms. If Grandfather took pride in any thing, it was in being the possessor of such an honorable and historic elbow chair.

"I know not precisely who next got possession of the chair, after Governor Vane went back to England," said Grandfather. "But there is reason to believe that President Dunster sat in it, when he held the first commencement at Harvard College. You have often heard, children, how careful our forefathers were, to give their young people a good education. They had scarcely cut down trees enough to make room for their own dwellings, before they began to think of establishing a college. Their principal object was, to rear up pious and learned ministers; and hence old writers call Harvard College a school of the prophets."

"Is the college a school of the prophets now?" asked Charley.

"It is a long while since I took my degree, Charley. You must ask some of the recent graduates," answered Grandfather. "As I was telling you, President Dunster sat in Grandfather's chair in 1642, when he conferred the degree of bachelor of arts on nine young men. They were the first in America, who had received that honor. And now, my dear auditors, I must confess that there are contradictory statements and some uncertainty about the adventures of the chair, for a period of almost ten years. Some say that it was occupied by your own ancestor, William Hawthorne, first Speaker of the House† of Representatives. I have nearly satisfied myself, however, that during most of this questionable period, it was literally the Chair of State. It gives me much pleasure to imagine that several successive governors of Massachusetts sat in it at the council board."

"But, Grandfather," interposed Charley, who was a matter-of-fact little person, "what reason have you to imagine so?"

"Pray do imagine it, Grandfather," said Laurence.

"With Charley's permission, I will," replied Grandfather, smiling. "Let us consider it settled, therefore, that Winthrop, Bellingham, Dudley, and Endicott, each of them, when chosen governor, took his seat in our great chair on election day. In this chair, likewise, did those excellent governors preside, while holding consultations with the chief councilors of the province, who were styled Assistants. The governor sat in this chair, too, whenever messages were brought to him from the chamber of Representatives."

And here Grandfather took occasion to talk, rather tediously, about the nature and forms of government that established themselves, almost spontaneously, in Massachusetts and the other New England colonies. Democracies† were the natural growth of the new world. As to Massachusetts, it was at first intended that the colony should be governed by a council in London. But, in a little while, the people had the whole power in their own hands, and chose annually the governor, the counsellors, and the representatives†. The people of old England had never enjoyed any thing like the liberties and privileges, which the settlers of New England now possessed. And they did not adopt these modes of government after long study, but in simplicity, as if there were no other way for people to be ruled.

"But, Laurence," continued Grandfather, "when you want instruction on these points, you must seek it in Mr. Bancroft's‡

HARVARD COLLEGE - 'SCHOOL OF THE PROPHETS'

History. I am merely telling the history of a chair. To proceed. The period during which the governors sat in our chair, was not very full of striking incidents. The province was now established on a secure foundation; but it did not increase so rapidly as at first, because the Puritans were no longer driven from England by persecution. However, there was still a quiet and natural growth. The legislature incorporated towns, and made new purchases of lands from the Indians. A very memorable event took place in 1643. The colonies of Massachusetts, Plymouth, Connecticut, and New Haven, formed a union, for the purpose of assisting each other in difficulties, and for mutual defense against their enemies. They called themselves the United Colonies of New England."

"Were they under a government like that of the United States?" inquired Laurence.

"No," replied Grandfather, "the different colonies did not compose one nation together; it was merely a confederacy among the governments. It somewhat resembled the league of the Amphictyons,† which you remember in Grecian history. But to return to our chair. In 1644 it was highly honored; for Governor Endicott sat in it, when he gave audience to an ambassador from the French governor of Acadie, or Nova Scotia. A treaty of peace, between Massachusetts and the French colony, was then signed."

"Did England allow Massachusetts to make war and peace with foreign countries?" asked Laurence.

"Massachusetts, and the whole of New England, was then almost independent of the mother country," said Grandfather. "There was now a civil war in England; and the king, as you may well suppose, had his hands full at home, and could pay but little attention to these remote colonies. When the Parliament got the power into their hands, they likewise had enough to do in keeping down the Cavaliers†. Thus New England, like a young and hardy lad, whose father and mother neglect it, was left to take care of itself. In 1649, King Charles was beheaded.‡ Oliver Cromwell then became Protector of England; and as he was a Puritan himself, and had risen by the valor of the English Puritans, he showed himself a loving and indulgent father to the Puritan colonies in America."

Grandfather might have continued to talk in this dull manner, nobody knows how long; but, suspecting that Charley would find the subject rather dry, he looked sideways at that vivacious little fellow, and saw him give an involuntary yawn. Whereupon, Grandfather proceeded with the history of the chair, and related a very entertaining incident, which will be found in the next chapter.

Chapter VI
The Pine Tree Shillings

"According to the most authentic records, my dear children," said Grandfather, "the chair, about this time, had the misfortune to break its leg. It was probably on account of this accident that it ceased to be the seat of the governors of Massachusetts; for, assuredly, it would have been ominous of evil to the commonwealth,† if the Chair of State had tottered upon three legs. Being therefore sold at auction–alas! what a vicissitude† for a chair that had figured in such high company–our venerable friend was knocked down to a certain Captain John Hull. This old gentleman, on carefully examining the maimed chair, discovered that its broken leg might be clamped with iron and made as serviceable as ever."

"Here is the very leg that was broken!" exclaimed Charley, throwing himself down on the floor to look at it. "And here are the iron clamps. How well it was mended!"

When they had all sufficiently examined the broken leg, Grandfather told them a story about Captain John Hull and

The Pine Tree Shillings

The Captain John Hull, aforesaid, was the mint-master of Massachusetts, and coined all the money that was made there. This was a new line of business: for, in the earlier days of the colony, the current coinage consisted of gold and silver money of England, Portugal, and Spain. These coins being scarce, the people were often forced to barter their commodities, instead of selling them.

For instance, if a man wanted to buy a coat, he perhaps exchanged a bearskin for it. If he wished for a barrel of molasses, he might purchase it with a pile of pine boards. Musket-bullets were used instead of farthings. The Indians had a sort of money, called wampum, which was made of clamshells; and this strange sort of specie† was likewise taken in payment of debts, by the English settlers. Bank bills had never been heard of. There was not money enough of any kind, in many parts of the country, to pay the salaries of the ministers; so that they sometimes had to take quintals† of fish, bushels of corn, or cords of wood, instead of silver or gold.

INDIAN WAMPUM

As the people grew more numerous, and their trade one with another increased, the want of current money was still more sensibly felt. To supply the demand, the general court passed a law for establishing a coinage of shillings, sixpences, and threepences. Captain John Hull was appointed to manufacture this money, and was to have about one shilling out of every twenty to pay him for the trouble of making them.

Hereupon, all the old silver in the colony was handed over to Captain John Hull. The battered silver cans and tankards,[†] I suppose, and silver buckles, and broken spoons, and silver buttons of worn out coats, and silver hilts of swords that had figured at court, all such curious old articles were doubtless thrown into the melting pot together. But by far the greater part of the silver consisted of bullion[†] from the mines of South America, which the English buccaneers–(who were little better than pirates)–had taken from the Spaniards, and brought to Massachusetts.

All this old and new silver being melted down and coined, the result was an immense amount of splendid shillings, sixpences, and threepences. Each had the date, 1652, on the one side, and the figure of a pine tree on the other. Hence they were called pine tree shillings. And for every twenty shillings that he coined, you will remember, Captain John Hull was entitled to put one shilling into his own pocket.

The magistrates soon began to suspect that the mint-master would have the best of the bargain. They offered him a large sum of money, if he would but give up that twentieth shilling, which he was continually dropping into his own pocket. But Captain Hull declared himself perfectly satisfied with the shilling. And well he might be; for so diligently did he labor, that, in a few years, his pockets, his money bags, and his strong box, were overflowing with pine tree shillings. This was probably the case when he came into possession of Grandfather's chair; and, as he had worked so hard at the mint, it was

PINE TREE SHILLING

certainly proper that he should have a comfortable chair to rest himself in.

When the mint-master had grown very rich, a young man, Samuel Sewell by name, came a-courting to his only daughter. His daughter,–whose name I do not know, but we will call her Betsey,–was a fine hearty damsel, by no means so slender as some young ladies of our own days. On the contrary, having always fed heartily on pumpkin pies, dough-nuts, Indian puddings, and other Puritan dainties, she was as round and plump as a pudding herself. With this round, rosy Miss Betsey, did Samuel Sewell fall in love. As he was a young man of good character, industrious in his business, and a member of the church, the mint-master very readily gave his consent.

"Yes–you may take her," said he, in his rough way; "and you'll find her a heavy burden enough!"

On the wedding day, we may suppose that honest John Hull dressed himself in a plum colored coat, all the buttons of which were made of pine tree shillings. The buttons of his waistcoat were sixpences; and the knees of his smallclothes† were buttoned with silver threepences. Thus attired, he sat with great dignity in Grandfather's chair; and, being a portly old gentleman, he completely filled it from elbow to elbow. On the opposite side of the room, between her bridesmaids, sat Miss Betsey. She was blushing with all her might, and looked like a full blown peony, or a great red apple.

There, too, was the bridegroom, dressed in a fine purple coat, and gold lace waistcoat, with as much other finery as the Puritan laws and customs would allow him to put on. His hair was cropped close to his head, because Governor

Endicott had forbidden any man to wear it below the ears. But he was a very personable young man; and so thought the bridesmaids and Miss Betsey herself.

The mint-master also was pleased with his new son-in-law; especially as he had courted Miss Betsey out of pure love, and had said nothing at all about her portion†. So when the marriage ceremony was over, Captain Hull whispered a word to two of his men-servants, who immediately went out, and soon returned, lugging in a large pair of scales. They were such a pair as wholesale merchants use, for weighing bulky commodities; and quite a bulky commodity was now to be weighed in them.

"Daughter Betsey," said the mint-master, "get into one side of these scales."

Miss Betsey,–or Mrs. Sewell, as we must now call her,–did as she was bid, like a dutiful child, without any question of the why and wherefore. But what her father could mean, unless to make her husband pay for her by the pound, (in which case she would have been a dear bargain,) she had not the least idea.

"And now," said honest John Hull to the servants, "bring that box hither."

The box, to which the mint-master pointed, was a huge, square, iron bound, oaken chest; it was big enough, my children, for all four of you to play at hide-and-seek in. The servants tugged with might and main, but could not lift this enormous receptacle, and were finally obliged to drag it across the floor. Captain Hull then took a key from his girdle, unlocked the chest, and lifted its ponderous lid. Behold! It was full to the brim of bright pine tree shillings,

MISS BETSEY HULL IN THE BALANCE

fresh from the mint; and Samuel Sewell began to think that his father-in-law had got possession of all the money in the Massachusetts treasury. But it was only the mint-master's honest share of the coinage.

Then the servants, at Captain Hull's command, heaped double handfuls of shillings into one side of the scales, while Betsey remained in the other. Jingle, jingle, went the shillings, as handful after handful was thrown in, till, plump and ponderous as she was, they fairly weighed the young lady from the floor.

"There, son Sewell!" cried the honest mint-master, resuming his seat in Grandfather's chair. "Take these shillings for my daughter's portion. Use her kindly, and thank Heaven for her. It is not every wife that's worth her weight in silver!"

***

The children laughed heartily at this legend, and would hardly be convinced but that Grandfather had made it out of his own head. He assured them faithfully, however, that he had found it in the pages of a grave historian, and had merely tried to tell it in a somewhat funnier style. As for Samuel Sewell, he afterwards became Chief Justice of Massachusetts.

"Well, Grandfather," remarked Clara, "if wedding portions now-a-days were paid as Miss Betsey's was, young ladies would not pride themselves upon an airy figure as many of them do."

Chapter VII

The Quakers and the Indians

When his little audience next assembled round the chair, Grandfather gave them a doleful history of the Quaker persecution, which began in 1656, and raged for about three years in Massachusetts.

He told them how, in the first place, twelve of the converts of George Fox, the first Quaker in the world, had come over from England. They seemed to be impelled by an earnest love for the souls of men, and a pure desire to make known what they considered a revelation from Heaven. But the rulers looked upon them as plotting the downfall of all government and religion. They were banished from the colony. In a little while, however, not only the first twelve had returned, but a multitude of other Quakers had come to rebuke the rulers, and to preach against the priests and steeple-houses.†

Grandfather described the hatred and scorn with which these enthusiasts were received. They were thrown into dungeons; they were beaten with many stripes, women as well as men; they were driven forth into the wilderness, and left to the tender mercies of wild beasts and Indians. The children were amazed to hear that the more the Quakers were scourged, and imprisoned, and banished, the more did the sect increase, both by the influx of strangers, and by converts from among the Puritans. But Grandfather told them that God had put something into the soul of man, which always turned the cruelties of the persecutor to nought.

He went on to relate that, in 1659, two Quakers, named William Robinson and Marmaduke Stephenson, were hanged at Boston. A woman had been sentenced to die with them, but was reprieved, on condition of her leaving the colony. Her name was Mary Dyer‡. In the year 1660 she returned to Boston, although she knew death awaited her

MARY DYER LED TO EXECUTION IN BOSTON COMMONS

there; and, if Grandfather had been correctly informed, an incident had then taken place, which connects her with our story. This Mary Dyer had entered the mint-master's dwelling, clothed in sackcloth and ashes, and seated herself in our great chair, with a sort of dignity and state. Then she proceeded to deliver what she called a message from Heaven; but in the midst of it, they dragged her to prison.

"And was she executed?" asked Laurence.

"She was," said Grandfather.

"Grandfather," cried Charley, clenching his fist, "I would have fought for that poor Quaker woman!"

"Ah! But if a sword had been drawn for her," said Laurence, "it would have taken away all the beauty of her death."

It seemed as if hardly any of the preceding stories had thrown such an interest around Grandfather's chair, as did the fact that the poor, persecuted, wandering Quaker woman had rested in it for a moment. The children were so much excited that Grandfather found it necessary to bring his account of the persecution to a close.

"In 1660, the same year in which Mary Dyer was executed," said he, "Charles the Second‡ was restored to the throne of his fathers. This king had many vices; but he would not permit blood to be shed, under pretence of religion, in any part of his dominions. The Quakers in England told him what had been done to their brethren in Massachusetts; and he sent orders to Governor Endicott to forbear all such proceedings in future. And so ended the Quaker persecution,‡–one of the most mournful passages in the history of our forefathers."

Grandfather then told his auditors that shortly after the

above incident, the great chair had been given by the mint-master to the Rev. Mr. John Eliot. He was the first minister of Roxbury. But besides attending to his pastoral duties there, he learned the language of the red men, and often went into the woods to preach to them. So earnestly did he labor for their conversion that he has always been called the apostle to the Indians. The mention of this holy man suggested to Grandfather the propriety of giving a brief sketch of the history of the Indians, so far as they were connected with the English colonists.

A short period before the arrival of the first Pilgrims at Plymouth, there had been a very grievous plague among the red men; and the sages and ministers of that day were inclined to the opinion that Providence had sent this mortality, in order to make room for the settlement of the English. But I know not why we should suppose that an Indian's life is less precious, in the eye of Heaven, than that of a white man. Be that as it may, death had certainly been very busy with the savage tribes.

INDIAN WIGWAM

In many places the English found the wigwams deserted, and the cornfields growing to waste, with none to harvest the grain. There were heaps of earth also, which, being dug open, proved to be Indian graves, containing bows and flint-headed spears and arrows; for the Indians buried the dead warrior's weapons along with him. In some spots, there were skulls and other human bones, lying unburied. In 1633, and the year afterwards, the smallpox broke out among the Massachusetts Indians, multitudes of whom died by this terrible disease of the old world. These misfortunes made them far less powerful than they had formerly been.

For nearly half a century after the arrival of the English, the red men showed themselves generally inclined to peace and amity†. They often made submission, when they might have made successful war. The Plymouth settlers, led by the famous Captain Miles Standish, slew some of them in 1623, without any very evident necessity for so doing. In 1636, and the following year, there was the most dreadful war that had yet occurred between the Indians and the English. The Connecticut settlers, assisted by a celebrated Indian chief, named Uncas,‡ bore the brunt of this war, with but little aid from Massachusetts. Many hundreds of the hostile Indians were slain, or burnt in their wigwams. Sassacus,‡ their sachem,† fled to another tribe, after his own people were defeated; but he was murdered by them, and his head was sent to his English enemies.

From that period, down to the time of King Philip's war, which will be mentioned hereafter, there was not much trouble with the Indians. But the colonists were always on their guard, and kept their weapons ready for the conflict.

"I have sometimes doubted," said Grandfather, when he had told these things to the children, "I have sometimes doubted whether there was more than a single man, among our forefathers, who realized that an Indian possesses a mind and a heart, and an immortal soul. That single man was John Eliot. All the rest of the early settlers seemed to think that the Indians were an inferior race of beings, whom the Creator had merely allowed to keep possession of this beautiful country, till the white men should be in want of it.

"Did the pious men of those days never try to make Christians of them?" asked Laurence.

"Sometimes, it is true," answered Grandfather, "the magistrates and ministers would talk about civilizing and converting the red people. But, at the bottom of their hearts, they would have had almost as much expectation of civilizing a wild bear of the woods, and making him fit for paradise. They felt no faith in the success of any such attempts, because they had no love for the poor Indians. Now Eliot was full of love for them, and therefore so full of faith and hope that he spent the labor of a lifetime in their behalf."

"I would have conquered them first, and then converted them," said Charley.

"Ah, Charley, there spoke the very spirit of our forefathers!" replied Grandfather. "But Mr. Eliot had a better spirit. He looked upon them as his brethren. He persuaded as many of them as he could, to leave off their idle and wandering habits, and to build houses, and cultivate the earth, as the English did. He established schools among them, and taught many of the Indians how to read. He taught them, likewise, how to pray. Hence they were called 'praying Indians.' Finally, having spent the best years of his life for their good, Mr. Eliot resolved to spend the remainder in doing them a yet greater benefit."

"I know what that was!" cried Laurence.

"He sat down in his study," continued Grandfather, "and began a translation of the Bible into the Indian tongue. It was while he was engaged in this pious work that the mint-master gave him our great chair. His toil needed it, and deserved it."

"Oh, Grandfather, tell us all about that Indian Bible!" exclaimed Laurence. "I have seen it in the library of the Athenæum‡; and the tears came into my eyes, to think that there were no Indians left to read it."

Chapter VIII
The Indian Bible

As Grandfather was a great admirer of the Apostle Eliot, he was glad to comply with the earnest request which Laurence had made, at the close of the last chapter. So he proceeded to describe how good Mr. Eliot labored, while he was at work upon

The Indian Bible

My dear children, what a task would you think it, even with a long lifetime before you, were you bidden to copy every chapter and verse, and word, in yonder great family Bible! Would not this be a heavy toil? But if the task were, not to write off the English Bible, but to learn a language, utterly unlike all other tongues,–a language which hitherto had never been learned, except by the Indians themselves, from their mothers' lips,–a language never written, and the strange words of which seemed inexpressible by letters;–if the task were, first, to learn this new variety of speech, and then to translate the Bible into it, and to do it so carefully, that not one idea throughout the holy book should be changed,–what would induce you to undertake this toil? Yet this was what the Apostle Eliot did.

It was a mighty work for a man, now growing old, to take upon himself. And what earthly reward could he expect from it? None; no reward on earth. But he believed that the red men were the descendants of those lost tribes of Israel of whom history has been able to tell us nothing, for thousands of years. He hoped that God had sent the English across the ocean, Gentiles as they were, to enlighten this benighted portion of His once chosen race. And when he should be summoned hence, he trusted to meet blessed spirits in another world, whose bliss would have been earned by his patient toil, in translating the Word of God. This hope and trust were far dearer to him, than any thing that earth could offer.

ARROWHEAD

Sometimes, while thus at work, he was visited by learned men, who desired to know what literary undertaking Mr. Elliot had in hand. They, like himself, had been bred in the studious cloisters of a university, and were supposed to possess all the erudition† which mankind has hoarded up from age to age. Greek and Latin were as familiar to them as the babble of their childhood. Hebrew was like their mother tongue. They had grown gray in study; their eyes were bleared with poring over print and manuscript by the light of the midnight lamp.

And yet, how much had they left unlearned! Mr. Eliot would put into their hands some of the pages, which he had been writing; and behold! The gray-headed men stammered over the long, strange words, like a little child in his first attempts to read. Then would the apostle call to him an Indian boy, one of his scholars, and show him the manuscript, which had so puzzled the learned Englishmen.

"Read this, my child," said he, "these are some brethren of mine, who would fain hear the sound of thy native tongue."

Then would the Indian boy cast his eyes over the mysterious page, and read it so skillfully that it sounded like wild music. It seemed as if the forest leaves were singing in the ears of his auditors, and as if the roar of distant streams were poured through the young Indian's voice. Such were the sounds amid which the language of the red man had been formed; and they were still heard to echo in it.

The lesson being over, Mr. Eliot would give the Indian boy an apple or a cake, and bid him leap forth into the open air, which his free nature loved. The apostle was kind to children, and even shared in their sports, sometimes. And when his visitors had bidden him farewell, the good man turned patiently to his toil again.

No other Englishman had ever understood the Indian character so well, nor possessed so great an influence over the New England tribes, as the apostle did. His advice and assistance must often have been valuable to his countrymen, in their transactions with the Indians. Occasionally, perhaps, the governor and some of the counsellors came to visit Mr. Eliot. Perchance they were seeking some method to circumvent the forest people. They inquired, it may be, how they could obtain possession of such and such a tract of their rich land. Or they talked of making the Indians their servants, as if God had destined them for perpetual bondage to the more powerful white man.

Perhaps, too, some warlike captain, dressed in his buff-coat,[†] with a corselet[†] beneath it, accompanied the governor and counsellors. Laying his hand upon his sword hilt, he would declare that the only method of dealing with the red men was to meet them with the sword drawn, and the musket presented.

But the apostle resisted both the craft of the politician, and the fierceness of the warrior.

"Treat these sons of the forest as men and brethren," he would say, "and let us endeavor to make them Christians. Their forefathers were of that chosen race, whom God delivered from Egyptian bondage. Perchance he has destined us to deliver the children from the more cruel bondage of ignorance and idolatry. Chiefly for this end, it may be, we were directed across the ocean."

When these other visitors were gone, Mr. Eliot bent himself again over the half-written page. He dared hardly relax a moment from his toil. He felt that, in the book which he was translating, there was a deep human, as well as heavenly wisdom, which would of itself suffice to civilize and refine the savage tribes. Let the Bible be diffused among them, and all earthly good would follow. But how slight a consideration was this, when he reflected that the eternal welfare of a whole race of men depended upon his accomplishment of the task which he had set himself! What if his hands should be palsied? What if his mind should lose its vigor? What if death should come upon him, ere the work were done? Then must the red man wander in the dark wilderness of heathenism for ever.

Impelled by such thoughts as these, he sat writing in the great chair, when the pleasant summer breeze came in through his open casement; and also when the fire of forest logs sent up its blaze and smoke, through the broad stone chimney, into the wintry air. Before the earliest bird sang, in the morning, the apostle's lamp was kindled; and, at midnight, his weary head was not yet upon its pillow. And at length, leaning back in the great chair, he could say to himself, with a holy triumph,–"The work is finished!"

It was finished. Here was a Bible for the Indians. Those long lost descendants of the ten tribes of Israel would now learn the history of their forefathers. That grace, which the ancient Israelites had forfeited, was offered anew to their children.

There is no impiety in believing that, when his long life was over, the apostle of the Indians was welcomed to the celestial abodes by the prophets of ancient days, and by those earliest apostles and evangelists, who had drawn their inspiration from the immediate presence of the Savior. They first had preached truth and salvation to the world. And Eliot, separated from them by many centuries, yet full of the same spirit, had borne the like message to the new world of the West. Since the first days of Christianity, there has been no man more worthy to be numbered in the brotherhood of the apostles, than Eliot.

***

"My heart is not satisfied to think," observed Laurence, "that Mr. Eliot's labors have done no good, except to a few Indians of his own time. Doubtless, he would not have regretted his toil, if it were the means of saving but a single soul. But it is a grievous thing to me, that he should have toiled so hard to translate the Bible, and now the language and the people are gone! The Indian Bible itself is almost the only relic of both."

"Laurence," said his Grandfather, "if ever you should doubt that man is capable of disinterested zeal for his brother's good, then remember how the apostle Eliot toiled. And if you should feel your own self-interest pressing upon your heart too closely, then think of Eliot's Indian Bible. It is good for the world that such a man has lived, and left this emblem of his life."

The tears gushed into the eyes of Laurence, and he acknowledged that Eliot had not toiled in vain. Little Alice put up her arms to Grandfather, and drew down his white head beside her own golden locks.

"Grandfather," whispered she, "I want to kiss good Mr. Eliot!"

And, doubtless, good Mr. Eliot would gladly receive the kiss of so sweet a child as little Alice, and would think it a portion of his reward in heaven.

Grandfather now observed that Dr. Francis had written a very beautiful *Life of Eliot,*‡ which he advised Laurence to peruse. He then spoke of King Philip's war, which began in 1675, and terminated with the death of King Philip, in the following year. Philip was a proud, fierce Indian, whom Mr. Eliot had vainly endeavored to convert to the Christian faith.

"It must have been a great anguish to the apostle," continued Grandfather, "to hear of mutual slaughter and outrage between his own countrymen, and those for whom he felt

ELIOT SPEAKS IN AN INDIAN CAMP

the affection of a father. A few of the praying Indians joined the followers of King Philip. A greater number fought on the side of the English. In the course of the war, the little community of red people whom Mr. Eliot had begun to civilize, was scattered, and probably never was restored to a flourishing condition. But his zeal did not grow cold; and only about five years before his death he took great pains in preparing a new edition of the Indian Bible."

"I do wish Grandfather," cried Charley, "you would tell us all about the battles in King Philip's war."

"Oh, no!" exclaimed Clara. "Who wants to hear about tomahawks and scalping knives!"

"No, Charley," replied Grandfather, "I have no time to spare in talking about battles. You must be content with knowing that it was the bloodiest war that the Indians had ever waged against the white men; and that, at its close, the English set King Philip's‡ head upon a pole."

"Who was the captain of the English?" asked Charley.

"Their most noted captain was Benjamin Church,‡–a very famous warrior," said Grandfather. "But I assure you, Charley, that neither Captain Church, nor any of the officers and soldiers who fought in King Philip's war, did any thing a thousandth part so glorious, as Mr. Eliot did, when he translated the Bible for the Indians."

"Let Laurence be the apostle," said Charley to himself, "and I will be the captain."

Chapter IX
No Longer Freemen

The children were now accustomed to assemble round Grandfather's chair, at all their unoccupied moments; and often it was a striking picture to behold the white-headed old sire, with this flowery wreath of young people around him. When he talked to them, it was the past speaking to the present,–or rather to the future, for the children were of a generation which had not become actual. Their part in life, thus far, was only to be happy, and to draw knowledge from a thousand sources. As yet, it was not their time to do.

Sometimes, as Grandfather gazed at their fair, unworldly countenances, a mist of tears bedimmed his spectacles. He almost regretted that it was necessary for them to know any thing of the past, or to provide aught for the future. He could have wished that they might be always the happy, youthful creatures, who had hitherto sported around his chair, without inquiring whether it had a history. It grieved him to think that his little Alice, who was a flower bud fresh from paradise, must open her leaves to the rough breezes of the world, or ever open them in any clime. So sweet a child she was that it seemed fit her infancy should be immortal!

But such repinings† were merely flitting shadows across the old man's heart. He had faith enough to believe, and

THE KING PROCLAIMED IN BOSTON

wisdom enough to know, that the bloom of the flower would be even holier and happier than its bud. Even within himself,-though Grandfather was now at that period of life, when the veil of mortality is apt to hang heavily over the soul,-still, in his inmost being, he was conscious of something that he would not have exchanged for the best happiness of childhood. It was a bliss to which every sort of earthly experience,-all that he had enjoyed or suffered, or seen, or heard, or acted, with the broodings of his soul upon the whole,-had contributed somewhat. In the same manner must a bliss, of which now they could have no conception, grow up within these children, and form a part of their sustenance for immortality.

So Grandfather, with renewed cheerfulness, continued his history of the chair, trusting that a profounder wisdom than his own would extract, from these flowers and weeds of Time, a fragrance that might last beyond all time.

At this period of the story, Grandfather threw a glance backward, as far as the year 1660. He spoke of the ill-concealed reluctance with which the Puritans in America had acknowledged the sway of Charles the Second, on his restoration to his father's throne. When death had stricken Oliver Cromwell, that mighty protector had no sincerer mourners than in New England. The new king had been more than a year upon the throne before his accession was proclaimed in Boston; although the neglect to perform the ceremony might have subjected the rulers to the charge of treason.

During the reign of Charles the Second, however, the American colonies had but little reason to complain of harsh or tyrannical treatment. But when Charles died, in 1685, and was succeeded by his brother James, the patriarchs of New England began to tremble. King James was a bigoted† Roman Catholic, and was known to be of an arbitrary temper. It was feared by all Protestants, and chiefly by the Puritans, that he would assume despotic† power, and attempt to establish Popery throughout his dominions. Our forefathers felt that they had no security either for their religion or their liberties.

The result proved that they had reason for their apprehensions. King James caused the charters of all the American colonies to be taken away.‡ The old charter of Massachusetts, which the people regarded as a holy thing, and as the foundation of all their liberties, was declared void. The colonists were now no longer freemen; they were entirely dependent on the king's pleasure. At first, in 1685, King James appointed Joseph Dudley, a native of Massachusetts, to be president of New England. But soon afterwards, Sir Edmund Andros, an officer of the English army, arrived, with a commission to be governor-general of New England and New York.

The king had given such powers to Sir Edmund Andros that there was now no liberty, nor scarcely any law, in the colonies over which he ruled. The inhabitants were not allowed to choose representatives, and consequently had no voice whatever in the government, nor control over the measures that were adopted. The counsellors, with whom the governor consulted on matters of state, were appointed by himself. This sort of government was no better than an absolute despotism.

"The people suffered much wrong, while Sir Edmund Andros ruled over them," continued Grandfather, "and they were apprehensive of much more. He had brought some soldiers with him from England, who took possession of the old fortress on Castle Island, and of the fortification on Fort Hill. Sometimes it was rumored that a general massacre of the inhabitants was to be perpetrated by these soldiers. There were reports, too, that all the ministers were to be slain or imprisoned."

"For what?" inquired Charley.

"Because they were the leaders of the people, Charley," said Grandfather. "A minister was a more formidable man than a general, in those days. Well; while these things were going on in America, King James had so misgoverned the people of England that they sent over to Holland for the Prince of Orange. He had married the king's daughter, and was therefore considered to have a claim to the crown. On his arrival in England, the Prince of Orange was proclaimed king, by the name of William the Third‡. Poor old King James made his escape to France."

SIR EDMUND ANDROS

Grandfather told how, at the first intelligence of the landing of the Prince of Orange in England, the people of Massachusetts rose in their strength, and overthrew the government of Sir Edmund Andros. He, with Joseph Dudley, Edmund Randolph, and his other principal adherents, were thrown into prison. Old Simon Bradstreet, who had been governor, when King James took away the charter, was called by the people to govern them again.

"Governor Bradstreet was a venerable old man, nearly ninety years of age," said Grandfather. "He came over with the first settlers, and had been the intimate companion of all those excellent and famous men who laid the foundation of our country. They were all gone before him to the grave; and Bradstreet was the last of the Puritans."

Grandfather paused a moment, and smiled, as if he had something very interesting to tell his auditors. He then proceeded:

"And now, Laurence,–now, Clara,–now, Charley,–now, my dear little Alice,–what chair do you think had been placed in the council chamber, for old Governor Bradstreet to take his seat in? Would you believe that it was this very chair in

YOUNG SIMON BRADSTREET

which grandfather now sits, and of which he is telling you the history?"

"I am glad to hear it, with all my heart!" cried Charley, after a shout of delight. "I thought Grandfather had quite forgotten the chair."

"It was a solemn and affecting sight," said Grandfather, "when this venerable patriarch, with his white beard flowing down upon his breast, took his seat in his Chair of State. Within his remembrance, and even since his mature age, the site where now stood the populous town, had been a wild and forest-covered peninsula. The province, now so fertile, and spotted with thriving villages, had been a desert wilderness. He was surrounded by a shouting multitude, most of whom had been born in the country which he had helped to found. They were of one generation, and he of another. As the old man looked upon them, and beheld new faces everywhere, he must have felt that it was now time for him to go, whither his brethren had gone before him."

"Were the former governors all dead and gone?" asked Laurence.

"All of them," replied Grandfather. "Winthrop had been dead forty years. Endicott died, a very old man, in 1665. Sir Henry Vane was beheaded in London, at the beginning of the reign of Charles the Second. And Haynes, Dudley, Bellingham and Leverett, who had all been governors of Massachusetts, were now likewise in their graves. Old Simon Bradstreet was the sole representative of that departed brotherhood. There was no other public man remaining to connect the ancient system of government and manners with the new system, which was about to take its place.

The era of the Puritans was now completed."

"I am sorry for it," observed Laurence; "for, though they were so stern, yet it seems to me that there was something warm and real about them. I think, Grandfather, that each of these old governors should have his statue set up in our State House, sculptured out of the hardest of New England granite."

"It would not be amiss, Laurence," said Grandfather; "but perhaps clay, or some other perishable material, might suffice for some of their successors. But let us go back to our chair. It was occupied by Governor Bradstreet from April, 1689, until May, 1692. Sir William Phips then arrived in Boston, with a new charter from King William, and a commission to be governor."

Chapter X
The Sunken Treasure

"And what became of the chair," inquired Clara.

"The outward aspect of our chair," replied Grandfather, "was now somewhat the worse for its long and arduous services. It was considered hardly magnificent enough to be allowed to keep its place in the council chamber of Massachusetts. In fact, it was banished as an article of useless lumber. But Sir William Phips happened to see it and being much pleased with its construction, resolved to take the good old chair into his private mansion. Accordingly, with his own gubernatorial† hands, he repaired one of its arms, which had been slightly damaged".

"Why, Grandfather, here is the very arm!" interrupted Charley, in great wonderment. "And did Sir William Phips put in these screws with his own hands? I am sure, he did it beautifully! But how came a governor to know how to mend a chair?"

"I will tell you a story about the early life of Sir William Phips," said Grandfather. "You will then perceive that he well knew how to use his hands."

So Grandfather related the wonderful and true tale of

The Sunken Treasure

Picture to yourselves, my dear children, a handsome, old-fashioned room, with a large, open cupboard at one end, in which is displayed a magnificent gold cup, with some other splendid articles of gold and silver plate. In another part of the room, opposite to a tall looking glass, stands our beloved chair, newly polished, and adorned with a gorgeous cushion of crimson velvet tufted with gold.

In the chair sits a man of strong and sturdy frame, whose face has been roughened by northern tempests, and blackened by the burning sun of the West Indies. He wears an immense periwig,† flowing down over his shoulders. His coat has a wide embroidery of golden foliage; and his waistcoat, likewise, is all flowered over and bedizened† with gold. His red, rough hands, which have done many a good day's work with the hammer and adze, are half covered by the delicate lace ruffles at his wrists. On a table lies his silver-hilted sword, and in a corner of the room stands his gold-headed cane, made of a beautifully polished West Indian wood.

GOLD CUP

Somewhat such an aspect as this, did Sir William Phips present, when he sat in Grandfather's chair, after the king had appointed him governor of Massachusetts. Truly, there was need that the old chair should be varnished, and decorated with a crimson cushion, in order to make it suitable for such a magnificent looking personage.

But Sir William Phips had not always worn a gold embroidered coat, nor always sat so much at his ease as he did in Grandfather's chair. He was a poor man's son, and was born in the province of Maine, where he used to tend sheep upon the hills, in his boyhood and youth. Until he had grown to be a man, he did not even know how to read and write. Tired of tending sheep, he next apprenticed himself to a ship carpenter, and spent about four years in hewing the crooked limbs of oak trees into knees† for vessels.

In 1673, when he was twenty-two years old, he came to Boston, and soon afterwards was married to a widow lady, who had property enough to set him up in business. It was not long, however, before he lost all the money that he had acquired by his marriage, and became a poor man again. Still, he was not discouraged. He often told his wife that, some time or other, he should be very rich, and would build a "fair brick house" in the Green Lane of Boston.

Do not suppose, children, that he had been to a fortune teller to inquire his destiny. It was his own energy and spirit of enterprise, and his resolution to lead an industrious life that made him look forward with so much confidence to better days.

Several years passed away; and William Phips had not yet gained the riches which he promised to himself. During this time he had begun to follow the sea for a living. In the year 1684, he happened to hear of a Spanish ship, which had been cast away near the Bahama Islands, and which was supposed to contain a great deal of gold and silver. Phips went to the place in a small vessel, hoping that he should be able to recover some of the treasure from the wreck. He did not succeed, however, in fishing up gold and silver enough to pay the expenses of his voyage.

But, before he returned, he was told of another Spanish ship or galleon, which had been cast away near Puerto de la Plata. She had now lain as much as fifty years beneath the waves. This old ship had been laden with immense wealth; and, hitherto, nobody had thought of the possibility of recovering any part of it from the deep sea, which was rolling and tossing it about. But though it was now an old story, and the most aged people had almost forgotten that such a vessel had been wrecked, William Phips resolved that the sunken treasure should again be brought to light.

He went to London, and obtained admittance to King James, who had not yet been driven from his throne. He told the king of the vast wealth that was lying at the bottom of the sea. King James listened with attention, and thought this a fine opportunity to fill his treasury with Spanish gold. He appointed William Phips to be captain of a vessel, called the *Rose Algier*, carrying eighteen guns and ninety-five men. So now he was Captain Phips of the English navy.

Captain Phips sailed from England in the *Rose Algier*, and cruised for nearly two years in the West Indies, endeavoring to find the wreck of the Spanish ship. But the sea is so wide and deep that it is no easy matter to discover the exact spot where a sunken vessel lies. The prospect of success seemed very small; and most people would have thought that Captain Phips was as far from having money enough to build a "fair brick house," as he was while he tended sheep.

The seamen of the *Rose Algier* became discouraged, and gave up all hope of making their fortunes by discovering the

SIR WILLIAM PHIPS RECOVERING SUNKEN TREASURE

Spanish wreck. They wanted to compel Captain Phips to turn pirate. There was a much better prospect, they thought, of growing rich by plundering vessels, which still sailed the sea, than by seeking for a ship that had lain beneath the waves full half a century. They broke out in open mutiny, but were finally mastered by Phips, and compelled to obey his orders. It would have been dangerous, however, to continue much longer at sea with such a crew of mutinous sailors; and, besides, the *Rose Algier* was leaky and unseaworthy. So Captain Phips judged it best to return to England.

Before leaving the West Indies, he met with a Spaniard, an old man, who remembered the wreck of the Spanish ship, and gave him directions how to find the very spot. It was on a reef of rocks a few leagues from Puerto de la Plata.

On his arrival in England, therefore, Captain Phips solicited the king to let him have another vessel, and send him back again to the West Indies. But King James, who had probably expected that the *Rose Algier* would return laden with gold, refused to have anything more to do with the affair. Phips might never have been able to renew the search, if the Duke of Albemarle, and some other noblemen had not lent their assistance. They fitted out a ship and gave the command to Captain Phips. He sailed from England, and arrived safely at Puerto de la Plata, where he took an adze and assisted his men to build a large boat.

The boat was intended for the purpose of going closer to the reef of rocks than a large vessel could safely venture. When it was finished, the Captain sent several men in it, to examine the spot where the Spanish ship was said to have been wrecked. They were accompanied by some Indians, who were skillful divers, and could go down a great way into the depths of the sea.

The boat's crew proceeded to the reef of rocks, and rowed round and round it, a great many times. They gazed down into the water, which was so transparent that it seemed as if they could have seen the gold and silver at the bottom, had there been any of those precious metals there. Nothing, however, could they see; nothing more valuable than a curious sea shrub, which was growing beneath the water, in a crevice of the reef of rocks. It flaunted to and fro with the swell and reflux of the waves, and looked as bright and beautiful as if its leaves were gold.

"We won't go back empty handed," cried an English sailor; and then he spoke to one of the Indian divers. "Dive down and bring me that pretty sea shrub there. That's the only treasure we shall find!"

Down plunged the diver, and soon rose dripping from the water, holding the sea shrub in his hand. But he had learnt some news at the bottom of the sea.

"There are some ship's guns," said he, the moment he had drawn breath, "some great cannon among the rocks, near where the shrub was growing."

No sooner had he spoken, than the English sailors knew that they had found the very spot where the Spanish galleon had been wrecked so many years before. The other Indian divers immediately plunged over the boat's side, and swam headlong down, groping among the rocks and sunken cannon. In a few moments one of them rose above the water, with a heavy lump of silver in his arms. That single lump was worth more than a thousand dollars. The sailors took it into the boat, and then rowed back as speedily as they could, being in haste to inform Captain Phips of their good luck.

But, confidently as the Captain had hoped to find the Spanish wreck, yet now that it was really found, the news seemed too good to be true. He could not believe it till the sailors showed him the lump of silver.

"Thanks be to God!" then cries Captain Phips. "We shall every man of us make our fortunes!"

Hereupon the Captain and all the crew set to work, with iron rakes and great hooks and lines, fishing for gold and silver at the bottom of the sea. Up came the treasure in abundance. Now they beheld a table of solid silver, once the property of an old Spanish Grandee†. Now they found a sacramental vessel, which had been destined as a gift to some Catholic church. Now they drew up a golden cup, fit for the king of Spain to drink his wine out of. Perhaps the bony hand of its former owner had been grasping the precious cup, and was drawn up along with it. Now their rakes or fishing lines were loaded with masses of silver bullion. There were also precious stones among the treasure, glittering and sparkling, so that it is a wonder how their radiance could have been concealed.

There is something sad and terrible in the idea of snatching all this wealth from the devouring ocean, which had possessed it for such a length of years. It seems as if men had no right to make themselves rich with it. It ought to have been left with the skeletons of the ancient Spaniards, who had been drowned when the ship was wrecked, and whose bones were now scattered among the gold and silver.

But Captain Phips and his crew were troubled with no such thoughts as these. After a day or two they lighted on another part of the wreck, where they found a great many bags of silver dollars. But nobody could have guessed that these were moneybags. By remaining so long in the saltwater, they had become covered over with a crust which had the appearance of stone, so that it was necessary to break them in pieces with hammers and axes. When this was done, a stream of silver dollars gushed out upon the deck of the vessel.

The whole value of the recovered treasure, plate, bullion, precious stones, and all, was estimated at more than two millions of dollars. It was dangerous even to look at such a vast amount of wealth. A sea captain, who had assisted Phips in the enterprise, utterly lost his reason at the sight of it. He died two years afterwards, still raving about the treasures that lie at the bottom of the sea. It would have been better for this man, if he had left the skeletons of the shipwrecked Spaniards in quiet possession of their wealth.

Captain Phips and his men continued to fish up plate, bullion, and dollars, as plentifully as ever, till their provisions grew short. Then, as they could not feed upon gold and silver any more than old King Midas[‡] could, they found it necessary to go in search of better sustenance. Phips resolved to return to England. He arrived there in 1687, and was received with great joy by the Duke of Albemarle and the other English lords, who had fitted out the vessel. Well they might rejoice; for they took by far the greater part of the treasure to themselves.

The Captain's share, however, was enough to make him comfortable for the rest of his days. It also enabled him to fulfil his promise to his wife, by building a "fair brick house," in the Green Lane of Boston. The Duke of Albemarle sent Mrs. Phips a magnificent gold cup, worth at least five thousand dollars. Before Captain Phips left London, King James made him a knight; so that, instead of the obscure ship carpenter who had formerly dwelt among them, the inhabitants of Boston welcomed him on his return, as the rich and famous Sir William Phips.

COUNTING HIS MONEY

Chapter XI
What the Chair Had Known

"Sir William Phips," continued Grandfather, "was too active and adventurous a man to sit still in the quiet enjoyment of his good fortune. In the year 1690, he went on a military expedition against the French colonies in America, conquered the whole province of Acadie, and returned to Boston with a great deal of plunder."

"Why, grandfather, he was the greatest man that ever sat in the chair!" cried Charley.

"Ask Laurence what he thinks," replied Grandfather with a smile. "Well; in the same year, Sir William took command of an expedition against Quebec, but did not succeed in capturing the city. In 1692, being then in London, King William the Third appointed him governor of Massachusetts. And now, my dear children, having followed Sir William Phips through all his adventures and hardships, till we find him comfortably seated in Grandfather's chair, we will here bid him farewell. May he be as happy in ruling a people, as he was while he tended sheep!"

Charley, whose fancy had been greatly taken by the adventurous disposition of Sir William Phips, was eager to know how he had acted, and what happened to him while he held the office of governor. But Grandfather had made up his mind to tell no more stories for the present.

"Possibly, one of these days, I may go on with the adventures of the chair," said he. "But its history becomes very obscure just at this point; and I must search into some old books and manuscripts, before proceeding further. Besides, it is now a good time to pause in our narrative; because the new charter, which Sir William Phips brought over from England, formed a very important epoch in the history of the province."

"Really, Grandfather," observed Laurence, "this seems to be the most remarkable chair in the world. Its history cannot be told without intertwining it with the lives of distinguished men, and the great events that have befallen the country."

"True, Laurence," replied Grandfather, smiling, "We must write a book, with some such title as this,–*Memoirs of My Own Times*, by Grandfather's Chair."

"That would be beautiful!" exclaimed Laurence, clapping his hands.

"But, after all," continued Grandfather, "any other old chair, if it possessed memory, and a hand to write its recollections, could record stranger stories than any that I have told you. From generation to generation, a chair sits familiarly in the midst of human interests, and is witness to the most secret and confidential intercourse,† that mortal man can hold with his fellow. The human heart may best be read in the fireside chair. And as to external events, Grief and Joy keep a continual vicissitude around it and within it. Now we see the glad face and glowing form of Joy, sitting merrily in the old chair, and throwing a warm firelight radiance over all the household. Now, while we thought not of it, the dark clad mourner, Grief, has stolen into the place of Joy, but not to retain it long. The imagination can hardly grasp so wide a subject, as is embraced in the experience of a family chair."

SIR WILLIAM PHIPS BEFORE QUEBEC

"It makes my breath flutter,–my heart thrill,–to think of it," said Laurence. "Yes; a family chair must have a deeper history than a Chair of State."

"Oh, yes!" cried Clara, expressing a woman's feeling on the point in question, "The history of a country is not nearly so interesting as that of a single family would be."

"But the history of a country is more easily told," said Grandfather. "So, if we proceed with our narrative of the chair, I shall still confine myself to its connection with public events."

Good old Grandfather now rose and quitted the room, while the children remained gazing at the chair. Laurence, so vivid was his conception of past times, would hardly have deemed it strange, if its former occupants, one after another, had resumed the seat which they had each left vacant, such a dim length of years ago.

First, the gentle and lovely lady Arbella would have been seen in the old chair, almost sinking out of its arms, for very weakness; then Roger Williams, in his cloak and band, earnest, energetic, and benevolent; then the figure of Anne Hutchinson, with the like gesture as when she presided at the assemblages of women; then the dark, intellectual face of Vane, "young in years, but in sage counsel old." Next would have appeared the successive governors, Winthrop, Dudley, Bellingham, and Endicott, who sat in the chair, while it was a Chair of State. Then its ample seat would have been pressed by the comfortable, rotund corporation of the honest mint-master. Then the half-frenzied shape of Mary Dyer, the persecuted Quaker woman, clad in sackcloth and ashes, would have rested in it for a moment. Then the holy apostolic form of Eliot would have sanctified it. Then would have arisen, like the shade of departed Puritanism, the venerable dignity of the white-bearded Governor Bradstreet. Lastly, on the gorgeous crimson cushion of Grandfather's chair, would have shone the purple and golden magnificence of Sir William Phips.

But, all these, with the other historic personages, in the midst of whom the chair had so often stood, had passed, both in substance and shadow, from the scene of ages. Yet here stood the chair, with the old Lincoln coat of arms, and the oaken flowers and foliage, and the fierce lion's head at the summit, the whole, apparently, in as perfect preservation as when it had first been placed in the Earl of Lincoln's Hall. And what vast changes of society and of nations had been wrought by sudden convulsions or by slow degrees, since that era!

"This chair has stood firm when the thrones of kings were overturned!" thought Laurence. "Its oaken frame has proved stronger than many frames of government!"

More the thoughtful and imaginative boy might have mused; but now a large yellow cat, a great favorite with all the children, leaped in at the open window. Perceiving that Grandfather's chair was empty, and having often before experienced its comforts, puss laid herself quietly down upon the cushion. Laurence, Clara, Charley, and little Alice, all laughed at the idea of such a successor to the worthies of old times.

"Pussy," said little Alice, putting out her hand, into which the cat laid a velvet paw, "you look very wise. Do tell us a story about Grandfather's Chair!"

Appendix I: Extracts from *The Life of John Eliot*

By Convers Francis

Mr. Eliot had been for some time assiduously[†] employed in learning the Indian language. To accomplish this, he secured the assistance of one of the natives, who could speak English. Eliot, at the close of his *Indian Grammar*, mentions him as "a pregnant-witted young man, who had been a servant in an English house, who pretty well understood his own language, and had a clear pronunciation." He took this Indian into his family, and by constant intercourse with him soon became sufficiently conversant[†] with the vocabulary and construction of the language to translate the Ten Commandments, the Lord's Prayer, and several passages of Scripture, besides composing exhortations and prayers.

Mr. Eliot must have found his task anything but easy or inviting. He was to learn a dialect, in which he could be assisted by no affinity[†] with the languages he already knew. He was to do this without the help of any written or printed specimens, with nothing in the shape of a grammar or analysis, but merely by oral communication with his Indian instructor, or with other natives, who, however comparatively intelligent, must from the nature of the case have been very imperfect teachers. He applied himself to the work with great patience and sagacity,[†] carefully noting the differences between the Indian and the English modes of construction words; and, having once got a clue to this, he pursued every noun and verb he could think of through all possible variations. In this way he arrived at analyses and rules, which he could apply for himself in a general manner.

Neal says that Eliot was able to speak the language intelligibly† after conversing with the Indian servant a few months. This, in a limited sense, may be true; but he is said to have been engaged two years in the process of learning, before he went to preach to the Indians. In that time he acquired a somewhat ready facility† in the use of that dialect, by means of which he was to carry the instructions of spiritual truth to the men of the forest, though as late as 1649 he still lamented† his want of skill in this respect.

Notice having been given of his intention [of instructing the Indians], Mr. Eliot, in company with three others, whose names are not mentioned, having implored the divine blessing on the undertaking, made his first visit to the Indians on the 28th of October, 1646, at a place afterwards called Nonantum; a spot that has the honor of being the first on which a civilized and Christian settlement of Indians was effected within the English colonies of North America. This name was given to the high grounds in the northeast part of Newton, and to the bounds of that town and Watertown. At a short distance from the wigwams, they were met by Waban, a leading man among the Indians at that place, accompanied by others, and were welcomed with "English salutations." Waban, who is described as "the chief minister of justice among them," had before shown a better disposition than any other native to receive the religious instruction of the Christians, and had voluntarily proposed to have his eldest son educated by them. His son had been accordingly placed at school in Dedham, whence he had now come to attend the meeting.

The Indians assembled in Waban's wigwam; and thither Mr.

Eliot and his friends were conducted. When the company were all collected and quiet, a religious service was begun with prayer. This was uttered in English; the reason for which, as given by Mr. Eliot and his companions, was that he did not then feel sufficiently acquainted with the Indian language to use it in that service.

The same difficulty would not occur in preaching, since for this, we may suppose, he had sufficiently prepared his thoughts and expressions to make his discourse intelligible on all important points; and if he should, in some parts, fail of being understood, he could repeat or correct himself, till he should succeed better. Besides, he took with him an interpreter, who was frequently able to express his instructions more distinctly than he could himself. Though the prayer was unintelligible to the Indians, yet, as they knew it might not be without an effect in subduing their feeling so as to prepare them better to listen to the preaching.

Mr. Eliot then began his sermon, or address, from Ezekiel 37:9, 10‡. The word 'wind', in this passage, suggested to the minds of some, who afterwards gave an account of this meeting, a coincidence which might, in the spirit of the times, be construed† into a special appointment of Providence†. The name of 'Waban' signified, in the Indian tongue, 'wind'; so that when the preacher uttered the words, "say to the wind," it was as if he had proclaimed, "say to Waban." As this man afterwards exerted much influence in awaking the attention of his fellow savages to Christianity, it might seem that in this first visit of the messengers of the gospel he was singled out by a special call to work in the cause. It is not surprising that the Indians were struck at the coincidence. Mr. Eliot gave no countenance† to a superstitious use of the circumstance, and took care to tell them that, when he chose his text, he had no thought of any such application.

The sermon was an hour and a quarter long. One cannot but

suspect that Mr. Eliot injudiciously crowded too much into one address. It would seem to have been better, for the first time at least, to have given a shorter sermon, and to have touched upon fewer subjects. But he was doubtless borne on by his zeal† to do much in a good cause; and, as we have reason to think, by the attentive, though vague, curiosity of the Indians.

Thus ended a conference three hours long, at the end of which the Indians affirmed that they were not weary, and requested their visitors to come again. They expressed a wish to build a town and live together. Mr. Eliot promised to intercede† for them with the court. He and his companions then gave the men some tobacco, and the children some apples, and bade them farewell.

A fortnight afterwards, on the 11th of November, Mr. Eliot

ELIOT, THE FIRST MISSIONARY AMONG THE INDIANS

and his friends repeated their visit to the wigwam of Waban. This meeting was more numerous than the former. The religious service was opened, as before, with a prayer in English. This was followed by a few brief and plain questions addressed to the children, admitting short and easy answers. The children seemed well disposed to listen and learn. To encourage them, Mr. Eliot gave them occasionally an apple or a cake; and the adults were requested to repeat to them the instructions that had been given. He then preached to the assembly in their own language, telling them that he had come to bring them good news from God, and show them how wicked men might become good and happy; and, in general, discoursing on nearly the same topics as he had treated at his first visit.

Part Two

1692-1763
Famous People

The Second Epoch of Grandfather's Chair

Chapter I
The Chair in the Firelight

"Oh Grandfather, dear Grandfather," cried little Alice, "pray tell us some more stories about your chair!"

How long a time had fled, since the children had felt any curiosity to hear the sequel of this venerable chair's adventures! Summer was now past and gone, and the better part of autumn likewise. Dreary, chill November was howling, out of doors, and vexing the atmosphere with sudden showers of wintry rain, or sometimes with gusts of snow that rattled like small pebbles against the windows.

When the weather began to grow cool, Grandfather's chair had been removed from the summer parlor into a smaller and snugger room. It now stood by the side of a bright blazing wood fire. Grandfather loved a wood fire, far better than a grate of glowing anthracite,† or than the dull heat of an invisible furnace, which seems to think that it has done its duty in merely warming the house. But the wood fire is a kindly, cheerful, sociable spirit, sympathizing with mankind, and knowing that to create warmth is but one of the good offices which are expected from it. Therefore it dances on the hearth, and laughs broadly through the room, and plays a thousand antics, and throws a joyous glow over all the faces that encircle it.

In the twilight of the evening, the fire grew brighter and more cheerful. And thus, perhaps, there was something in Grandfather's heart that cheered him most with its warmth and comfort in the gathering twilight of old age. He had been gazing at the red embers, as intently as if his past life were all pictured there, or as if it were a prospect of the future world, when little Alice's voice aroused him.

"Dear Grandfather," repeated the little girl, more earnestly, "do talk to us again about your chair."

Laurence, and Clara, and Charley, and little Alice, had been attracted to other objects, for two or three months past. They had sported in the gladsome sunshine of the present, and so had forgotten the shadowy region of the past, in the midst of which stood Grandfather's chair. But now, in the autumnal twilight, illuminated by the flickering blaze of the wood fire, they looked at the old chair and thought that it had never before worn such an interesting aspect. There it stood, in the venerable majesty of more than two hundred years. The light from the hearth quivered upon the flowers and foliage that were wrought into its oaken back; and the lion's head at the summit seemed almost to move its jaws and shake its mane.

"Does little Alice speak for all of you?" asked Grandfather. "Do you wish me to go on with the adventures of the chair?"

"Oh, yes, yes, Grandfather!" cried Clara. "The dear old chair! How strange that we should have forgotten it so long!"

"Oh, pray begin, Grandfather," said Laurence; "for I think, when we talk about old times, it should be in the early evening before the candles are lighted. The shapes of the famous persons, who once sat in the chair, will be more apt to come back, and be seen among us, in this glimmer and pleasant gloom, than they would in the vulgar[†] daylight. And, besides, we can make pictures of all that you tell us, among the glowing embers and white ashes."

Our friend Charley, too, thought the evening the best time to hear Grandfather's stories, because he could not then be playing out of doors. So, finding his young auditors unanimous in their petition, the good old gentleman took up the narrative of the historic chair, at the point where he had dropped it.

Chapter II
The Salem Witches

"You recollect, my dear children," said Grandfather, "that we took leave of the chair in 1692, while it was occupied by Sir William Phips. This fortunate treasure seeker, you will remember, had come over from England, with King William's commission to be Governor of Massachusetts. Within the limits of this province were now included the old colony of Plymouth, and the territories of Maine and Nova Scotia. Sir William Phips had likewise brought a new charter from the king, which served instead of a constitution, and set forth the method in which the province was to be governed."

"Did the new charter allow the people all their former liberties?" inquired Laurence.

"No," replied Grandfather. "Under the first charter, the people had been the source of all power. Winthrop, Endicott, Bradstreet, and the rest of them, had been governors by the choice of the people, without any interference of the king. But henceforth the governor was to hold his station solely by the king's appointment, and during his pleasure; and the same was the case with the lieutenant-governor, and some other high officers. The people, however, were still allowed to choose representatives; and the governor's council was chosen by the general court."

"Would the inhabitants have elected Sir William Phips," asked Laurence, "if the choice of governor had been left to them?"

"He might probably have been a successful candidate," answered Grandfather; "for his adventures and military enterprises had gained him a sort of renown, which always goes a great way with the people. And he had many popular characteristics, being a kind, warm-hearted man, not ashamed of his low origin, nor haughty in his present elevation. Soon after his arrival, he proved that he did not blush to recognize his former associates."

"How was that?" inquired Charley.

"He made a grand festival at his new brick house," said Grandfather, "and invited all the ship carpenters of Boston to be his guests. At the head of the table, in our great chair, sat Sir William Phips himself, treating these hard-handed men as his brethren, cracking jokes with them, and talking familiarly about old times. I know not whether he wore his embroidered dress, but I rather choose to imagine that he had on a suit of rough clothes, such as he used to labor in, while he was Phips the ship carpenter."

"An aristocrat need not be ashamed of the trade," observed Laurence; "for the czar Peter the Great‡ once served an apprenticeship to it."

"Did Sir William Phips make as good a governor as he was a ship carpenter?" asked Charley.

"History says but little about his merits as a ship carpenter," answered Grandfather; "but, as a governor, a great deal of fault was found with him. Almost as soon as he assumed the government, he became engaged in a very frightful busi-

ARRESTING A WITCH

ness, which might have perplexed a wiser and better cultivated head than his. This was the witchcraft delusion‡."

And here Grandfather gave his auditors such details of this melancholy affair, as he thought it fit for them to know. They shuddered to hear that a frenzy, which led to the death of many innocent persons, had originated in the wicked arts of a few children. They belonged to the Rev. Mr. Parris, minister of Salem. These children complained of being pinched, and pricked with pins, and otherwise tormented by the shapes of men and women, who were supposed to have power to haunt them invisibly, both in darkness and daylight. Often, in the midst of their family and friends, the children would pretend to be seized with strange convulsions, and would cry out that the witches were afflicting them.

These stories spread abroad, and caused great tumult and alarm. From the foundation of New England, it had been the custom of the inhabitants, in all matters of doubt and difficulty, to look to their ministers for council. So they did now; but, unfortunately, the ministers and wise men were more deluded than the illiterate people. Cotton Mather, a very learned and eminent clergyman, believed that the whole country was full of witches and wizards, who had given up their hopes of heaven, and signed a covenant with the Evil One.

Nobody could be certain that his nearest neighbor, or most intimate friend, was not guilty of this imaginary crime. The number of those who pretended to be afflicted by witchcraft, grew daily more numerous; and they bore testimony against many of the best and worthiest people. A minister, named George Burroughs,‡ was among the accused. In the months of August and September, 1692, he, and nineteen other innocent men and women, were put to death. The place of execution was a high hill, on the outskirts of Salem; so that many of the sufferers, as they stood beneath the gallows, could discern their own habitations in the town.

The martyrdom of these guiltless persons seemed only to increase the madness. The afflicted now grew bolder in their accusations. Many people of rank and wealth were either thrown into prison, or compelled to flee for their lives. Among these were two sons of old Simon Bradstreet, the last of the Puritan governors. Mr. Willard, a pious minister of Boston, was cried out upon as a wizard, in open court. Mrs. Hale, the wife of the minister of Beverly, was likewise accused. Philip English, a rich merchant of Salem, found it necessary to take flight, leaving his property and business in confusion. But a short time afterwards, the Salem people were glad to invite him back.

"The boldest thing that the accusers did," continued Grandfather, "was to cry out against the governor's own beloved wife. Yes; the lady of Sir William Phips was accused of being a witch, and of flying through the air to attend witch meetings. When the governor heard this, he probably trembled, so that our great chair shook beneath him."

"Dear Grandfather," cried little Alice, clinging closer to his knee, "is it true that witches ever come in the nighttime to frighten little children?"

"No, no, dear little Alice," replied Grandfather. "Even if there were any witches, they would flee away from the presence of a pure-hearted child. But there are none; and our forefathers soon became convinced that they had been led into a terrible delusion. All the prisoners on account of witchcraft were set free. But the innocent dead could not be restored to life; and the hill where they were executed, will always remind people of the saddest and most humiliating passage in our history."

Grandfather then said that the next remarkable event, while Sir William Phips remained in the chair, was the arrival at Boston of an English fleet, in 1693. It brought an army, which was intended for the conquest of Canada. But a malignant disease, more fatal than the small-pox, broke out among the soldiers and sailors, and destroyed the greater part of them. The infection spread into the town of Boston, and made much havoc there. This dreadful sickness caused the governor, and Sir Francis Wheeler, who was commander of the British forces, to give up all thoughts of attacking Canada.

"Soon after this," said Grandfather, "Sir William Phips quarrelled with the captain of an English frigate, and also with the Collector of Boston[†]. Being a man of violent temper, he gave each of them a sound beating with his cane."

"He was a bold fellow," observed Charley, who was himself somewhat addicted to a similar mode of settling disputes.

"More bold than wise," replied Grandfather; "for complaints were carried to the king, and Sir William Phips was summoned to England, to make the best answer he could. Accordingly he went to London, where, in 1695, he was seized with a malignant fever, of which he died. Had he lived longer, he would probably have gone again in search of sunken treasure. He had heard of a Spanish ship, which was cast away in 1502, during the lifetime of Columbus. Bovadilla, Roldan, and many other Spaniards,[‡] were lost in her, together with the immense wealth of which they had robbed the South American kings."

"Why, Grandfather," exclaimed Laurence, "what magnificent ideas the governor had! Only think of recovering all that old treasure, which had lain almost two centuries under the sea! Methinks Sir William Phips ought to have been buried in the ocean, when he died; so that he might have gone down among the sunken ships, and cargoes of treasure, which he was always dreaming about in his lifetime."

"He was buried in one of the crowded cemeteries of London," said Grandfather. "As he left no children, his estate was inherited by his nephew, from whom is descended the present Marquis of Normandy. The noble Marquis is not aware, perhaps, that the prosperity of his family originated in the successful enterprise of a New England ship carpenter."

Chapter III

The Old-Fashioned School

"At the death of Sir William Phips," proceeded Grandfather, "our chair was bequeathed to Mr. Ezekiel Cheever, a famous schoolmaster in Boston. This old gentleman came from London in 1637, and had been teaching school ever since; so that there were now aged men, grandfathers like myself, to whom Master Cheever had taught their alphabet. He was a person of venerable aspect, and wore a long white beard.

"Was the chair placed in his school?" asked Charley.

"Yes, in his school," answered Grandfather; "and we may safely say that it had never before been regarded with such awful reverence–no, not even when the old governors of Massachusetts sat in it. Even you, Charley, my boy, would have felt some respect for the chair, if you had seen it occupied by this famous schoolmaster."

And here Grandfather endeavored to give his auditors an idea how matters were managed in schools above a hundred years ago. As this will probably be an interesting subject to our readers, we shall make a separate sketch of it, and call it

The Old-Fashioned School

Now imagine yourselves, my children, in Master Ezekiel Cheever's schoolroom. It is a large, dingy room, with a sanded floor, and is lighted by windows that turn on hinges, and have little diamond-shaped panes of glass. The scholars sit on long benches, with desks before them. At one end of the room is a great fireplace, so very spacious that there is room enough for three or four boys to stand in each of the chimney corners. This was the good old fashion of fireplaces, when there was wood enough in the forests to keep people warm, without their digging into the bowels of the earth for coal.

It is a winter's day when we take our peep into the schoolroom. See what great logs of wood have been rolled into the fireplace, and what a broad, bright blaze goes leaping up the chimney! And every few moments, a vast cloud of smoke is puffed into the room, which sails slowly over the heads of the scholars, until it gradually settles upon the walls and ceiling. They are blackened with the smoke of many years already.

Next, look at our old historic chair! It is placed, you perceive, in the most comfortable part of the room, where the generous glow of the fire is sufficiently felt, without being too intensely hot. How stately the old chair looks, as if it remembered its many famous occupants, but yet were conscious that a greater man is sitting in it now! Do you see the venerable schoolmaster, severe in aspect, with a black scull cap on his head, like an ancient Puritan, and the snow of his white beard drifting down to his very girdle[†]? What boy would dare to play, or whisper, or even glance aside from his book, while Master Cheever is on the lookout, behind his spectacles! For such offenders, if any such there be, a rod of birch is hanging over the fireplace, and a heavy ferule† lies on the master's desk.

And now school is begun. What a murmur of multitudinous tongues, like the whispering leaves of a wind-stirred oak, as the scholars con† over their various tasks! Buzz, buzz, buzz! Amid just such a murmur has Master Cheever spent above sixty years: and long habit has made it as pleasant to him as the hum of a beehive, when the insects are busy in the sunshine.

Now a class in Latin is called to recite. Forth steps a row of queer-looking little fellows, wearing square-skirted coats, and small clothes, with buttons at the knee. They look like so many grandfathers in their second childhood. These lads are to be sent to Cambridge, and educated for the learned professions. Old Master Cheever has lived so long, and seen so many generations of schoolboys grow up to be men, that now he can almost prophesy what sort of a man each boy will be. One urchin shall hereafter be a doctor, and administer pills and potions, and stalk gravely through life, perfumed with asafetida.† Another shall wrangle at the bar, and fight

CHILDREN WITH HORNBOOKS

his way to wealth and honors, and in his declining age, shall be a worshipful member of his Majesty's council. A third–and he is the Master's favorite–shall be a worthy successor to the old Puritan ministers, now in their graves; he shall preach with great unction† and effect, and leave volumes of sermons, in print and manuscript, for the benefit of future generations.

But, as they are merely schoolboys now, their business is to construe Virgil‡. Poor Virgil, whose verses, which he took so much pains to polish, have been mis-scanned, and mis-parsed, and mis-interpreted, by so many generations of idle schoolboys! There, sit down, ye Latinists. Two or three of you, I fear, are doomed to feel the master's ferule.

Next comes a class in Arithmetic. These boys are to be the merchants, shopkeepers, and mechanics, of a future period. Hitherto, they have traded only in marbles and apples. Hereafter, some will send vessels to England for broadcloths and all sorts of manufactured wares, and to the West Indies for sugar, and rum, and coffee.

SCHOOLMASTER

Others will stand behind counters, and measure tape, and ribbon, and cambric,† by the yard. Others will upheave the blacksmith's hammer, or drive the plane over the carpenter's bench, or take the lapstone† and the awl, and learn the trade of shoemaking. Many will follow the sea, and become bold, rough sea captains.

This class of boys, in short, must supply the world with those active, skillful hands, and clear, sagacious heads, without which the affairs of life would be thrown into confusion, by the theories of studious and visionary men. Wherefore, teach them their multiplication table, good Master Cheever, and whip them well, when they deserve it; for much of the country's welfare depends on these boys!

But, alas! While we have been thinking of other matters, Master Cheever's watchful eye has caught two boys at play. Now we shall see awful times! The two malefactors† are summoned before the master's chair, wherein he sits, with the terror of a judge upon his brow. Our old chair is now a judgment seat. Ah, Master Cheever has taken down that terrible birch rod! Short is the trial–the sentence quickly passed–and now the judge prepares to execute it in person. Thwack! Thwack! Thwack! In those good old times, a schoolmaster's blows were well laid on.

See! The birch rod has lost several of its twigs, and will hardly serve for another execution. Mercy on us, what a bellowing the urchins make! My ears are almost deafened, though the clamor comes through the far length of a hundred and fifty years. There, go to your seats, poor boys; and do not cry, sweet little Alice; for they have ceased to feel the pain, a long time since.

And thus the forenoon passes away. Now it is twelve o'clock. The master looks at his great silver watch, and then with tiresome deliberation, puts the ferule into his desk. The little multitude await the word of dismissal, with almost irrepressible impatience.

"You are dismissed," says Master Cheever.

The boys retire, treading softly until they have passed the threshold; but, fairly out of the schoolroom, lo, what a joyous shout! What a scampering and trampling of feet! What a sense of recovered freedom, expressed in the merry uproar of all their voices! What care they for the ferule and birch rod now? Were boys created merely to study Latin and Arithmetic? No; the better purposes of their being are to sport, to leap, to run, to shout, to slide upon the ice, to snowball!

Happy boys! Enjoy your playtime now, and come again to study, and to feel the birch rod and the ferule, tomorrow; not till tomorrow, for today is Thursday lecture; and ever since the settlement of Massachusetts, there has been no school on Thursday afternoons. Therefore, sport, boys, while you may; for the morrow cometh, with the birch rod and the ferule; and after that, another morrow, with troubles of its own.

Now the master has set every thing to rights, and is ready to go home to dinner. Yet he goes reluctantly. The old man has spent so much of his life in the smoky, noisy, buzzing schoolroom, that when he has a holiday, he feels as if his place were lost, and himself a stranger in the world. But, forth he goes; and there stands our old chair, vacant and solitary, till good Master Cheever resumes his seat in it tomorrow morning.

"Grandfather," said Charley, "I wonder whether the boys did not use to upset the old chair, when the schoolmaster was out?"

"There is a tradition," replied Grandfather, "that one of its arms was dislocated, in some such manner. But I cannot believe that any schoolboy would behave so naughtily."

As it was now later than little Alice's usual bedtime, Grandfather broke off his narrative, promising to talk more about Master Cheever and his scholars, some other evening.

Chapter IV
Cotton Mather

Accordingly the next evening, Grandfather resumed the history of his beloved chair.

"Master Ezekiel Cheever," said he, "died in 1707, after having taught school about seventy years. It would require a pretty good scholar in arithmetic to tell how many stripes he had inflicted, and how many birch rods he had worn out, during all that time, in his fatherly tenderness for his pupils. Almost all the great men of that period, and for many years back, had been whipped into eminence by Master Cheever. Moreover, he had written a Latin Accidence,[†] which was used in schools more than half a century after his death; so that the good old man, even in his grave, was still the cause of trouble and stripes to idle schoolboys."

Grandfather proceeded to say that when Master Cheever died, he bequeathed the chair to the most learned man that was educated at his school, or that had ever been born in America. This was the renowned Cotton Mather, minister of the Old North Church in Boston.

"And author of *The Magnalia,* Grandfather, which we sometimes see you reading," said Laurence.

"Yes, Laurence," replied Grandfather. "*The Magnalia* is a strange, pedantic[†] history, in which true events and real personages move before the reader, with the dreamy aspect which they wore in Cotton Mather's singular mind. This huge volume, however, was written and published before our chair came into his possession. But, as he was the author of more books than there are days in the year, we may conclude that he wrote a great deal, while sitting in this chair."

"I am tired of these schoolmasters and learned men," said Charley. "I wish some stirring man that knew how to do something in the world, like Sir William Phips, would sit in the chair."

"Such men seldom have leisure to sit quietly in a chair," said Grandfather. "We must make the best of such people as we have."

As Cotton Mather was a very distinguished man, Grandfather took some pains to give the children a lively conception of his character. Over the door of his library were painted these words–BE SHORT–as a warning to visitors that they must not do the world so much harm, as needlessly to interrupt this great man's wonderful labors. On entering the room you would probably behold it crowd-

COTTON MATHER

ed, and piled, and heaped with books. There were huge, ponderous folios and quartos,† and little duodecimos,† in English, Latin, Greek, Hebrew, Chaldaic, and all other languages, that either originated at the confusion of Babel,‡ or have since come into use.

All these books, no doubt, were tossed about in confusion, thus forming a visible emblem of the manner in which their contents were crowded into Cotton Mather's brain. And in the middle of the room stood a table, on which, besides printed volumes, were strewn manuscript sermons, historical tracts, and political pamphlets, all written in such a queer, blind, crabbed, fantastical hand, that a writing master would have gone raving mad at the sight of them. By this table stood Grandfather's chair, which seemed already to have contracted an air of deep erudition, as if its cushion were stuffed with Latin, Greek, and Hebrew, and other hard matters.

In this chair, from one year's end to another, sat that prodigious bookworm, Cotton Mather, sometimes devouring a great book, and sometimes scribbling one as big. In Grandfather's younger days, there used to be a wax figure of him in one of the Boston museums, representing a solemn, dark-visaged person, in a minister's black gown, and with a black-letter volume before him.

"It is difficult, my children," observed Grandfather, "to make you understand such a character as Cotton Mather's, in whom there was so much good, and yet so many failings and frailties. Undoubtedly, he was a pious man. Often he kept fasts; and once, for three whole days, he allowed himself not a morsel of food, but spent the time in prayer and religious meditation. Many a live-long night did he watch and pray. These fasts and vigils made him meagre† and haggard, and probably caused him to appear as if he hardly belonged to the world."

"Was not the witchcraft delusion partly caused by Cotton Mather?" inquired Laurence.

"He was the chief agent of the mischief," answered Grandfather; "but we will not suppose that he acted otherwise than conscientiously. He believed that there were evil spirits all about the world. Doubtless he imagined that they were hidden in the corners and crevices of his library, and that they peeped out from among the leaves of many of his books, as he turned them over, at midnight. He supposed that these unlovely demons were everywhere, in the sunshine as well as in the darkness, and that they were hidden in men's hearts, and stole into their most secret thoughts."

Here Grandfather was interrupted by little Alice, who hid her face in his lap, and murmured a wish that he would not talk any more about Cotton Mather and the evil spirits. Grandfather kissed her, and told her that angels were the only spirits whom she had any thing to do with. He then spoke of the public affairs of the period.

A new war between France and England had broken out in 1702, and had been raging ever since. In the course of it, New England suffered much injury from the French and Indians, who often came through the woods from Canada, and assaulted the frontier towns. Villages were sometimes burnt, and the inhabitants slaughtered, within a day's ride of Boston. The people of New England had a bitter hatred against the French, not only for the mischief which they did

INDIAN ATTACK

with their own hands, but because they incited the Indians to hostility.

The New Englanders knew that they could never dwell in security, until the provinces of France should be subdued, and brought under the English government. They frequently, in time of war, undertook military expeditions against Acadia and Canada, and sometimes besieged the fortresses, by which those territories were defended. But the most earnest wish of their hearts was to take Quebec, and so get possession of the whole province of Canada. Sir William Phips had once attempted it, but without success.

Fleets and soldiers were often sent from England, to assist the colonists in their warlike undertakings. In 1710, Port Royal, a fortress of Acadia, was taken by the English. The next year, in the month of June, a fleet, commanded by Admiral Sir Hovenden Walker, arrived in Boston Harbor. On board of this fleet was the English General Hill, with seven regiments of soldiers, who had been fighting under the Duke of Marlborough, in Flanders. The government of Massachusetts was called upon to find provisions for the army and fleet, and to raise more men to assist in taking Canada.

What with recruiting and drilling of soldiers, there was now nothing but warlike bustle in the streets of Boston. The drum and fife, the rattle of arms, and the shouts of boys, were heard from morning till night. In about a month, the fleet set sail, carrying four regiments from New England and New York, besides the English soldiers. The whole army amounted to at least seven thousand men. They steered for the mouth of the river St. Lawrence.

"Cotton Mather prayed most fervently for their success," continued Grandfather, "both in his pulpit, and when he kneeled down in the solitude of his library, resting his face on our old chair. But Providence ordered the result otherwise. In a few weeks, tidings were received that eight or nine of the vessels had been wrecked in the St. Lawrence, and that above a thousand drowned soldiers had been washed ashore, on the banks of that mighty river. After this misfortune, Sir Hovenden Walker set sail for England; and many pious people began to think it a sin even to wish for the conquest of Canada."

"I would never give it up so," cried Charley.

"Nor did they, as we shall see," replied Grandfather. "However, no more attempts were made during this war, which came to a close in 1713. The people of New England were probably glad of some repose; for their young men had been made soldiers, till many of them were fit for nothing else. And those, who remained at home, had been heavily taxed to pay for the arms, ammunition, fortifications, and all the other endless expenses of a war. There was great need of the prayers of Cotton Mather, and of all pious men, not only on account of the sufferings of the people, but because the old moral and religious character of New England was in danger of being utterly lost."

"How glorious it would have been," remarked Laurence, "if our forefathers could have kept the country unspotted with blood."

"Yes," said Grandfather; "but there was a stern warlike spirit in them, from the beginning. They seem never to have thought of questioning either the morality or piety of war."

The next event, which Grandfather spoke of, was one that Cotton Mather, as well as most of the other inhabitants of New England, heartily rejoiced at. This was the accession of the Elector of Hanover to the throne of England, in 1714, on the death of Queen Anne. Hitherto, the people had been in continual dread that the male line of the Stuarts, who were descended from the beheaded King Charles and the banished King James, would be restored to the throne. In that case, as the Stuart family were Roman Catholics, it was supposed that they would attempt to establish their own religion throughout the British dominions. But the Elector of Hanover, and all his race, were Protestants; so that now the descendants of the old Puritans were relieved from many fears and disquietudes.

"The importance of this event," observed Grandfather, "was a thousand times greater than that of a Presidential election, in our own days. If the people dislike their president, they may get rid of him in four years; whereas, a dynasty of kings may wear the crown for an unlimited period."

The German elector was proclaimed king from the balcony of the Town House‡ in Boston, by the title of George the First, while the trumpets sounded and the people cried Amen. That night, the town was illuminated; and Cotton Mather threw aside book and pen, and left Grandfather's chair vacant, while he walked hither and thither to witness the rejoicings.

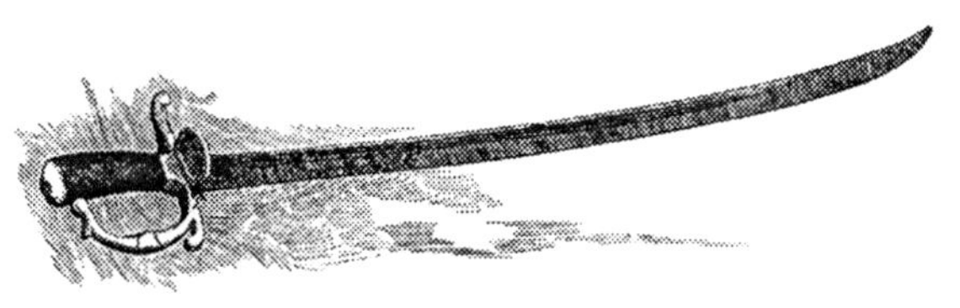

Chapter V
The Rejected Blessing

"Cotton Mather," continued Grandfather, "was a bitter enemy to Governor Dudley; and nobody exulted more than he, when that crafty politician was removed from the government, and succeeded by Colonel Shute‡. This took place in 1716. The new governor had been an officer in the renowned Duke of Marlborough's army, and had fought in some of the great battles in Flanders."

"Now, I hope," said Charley, "we shall hear of his doing great things."

"I am afraid you will be disappointed, Charley," answered Grandfather. "It is true that Colonel Shute had probably never led so unquiet a life while fighting the French, as he did now, while governing this province of Massachusetts Bay. But his troubles consisted almost entirely of dissensions with the legislature. The king had ordered him to lay claim to a fixed salary; but the representatives of the people insisted upon paying him only such sums, from year to year, as they saw fit."

Grandfather here explained some of the circumstances that made the situation of a colonial governor so difficult and irksome. There was not the same feeling towards the chief magistrate now that had existed while he was chosen by the free suffrages of the people. It was felt that as the king appointed the governor, and as he held his office during the king's pleasure, it would be his great object to please the king. But the people thought that a governor ought to have nothing in view but the best interests of those whom he governed.

"The governor," remarked Grandfather, "had two masters to serve–the king, who appointed him, and the people, on whom he depended for his pay. Few men in this position would have ingenuity enough to satisfy either party. Colonel Shute, though a good-natured, well-meaning man, succeeded so ill with the people, that in 1722, he suddenly went away to England, and made complaint to King George. In the mean time, Lieutenant-Governor Dummer‡ directed the affairs of the province, and carried on a long and bloody war with the Indians."

"But where was our chair, all this time?" asked Clara.

"It still remained in Cotton Mather's library," replied Grandfather; "and I must not omit to tell you an incident, which is very much to the honor of this celebrated man. It is the more proper, too, that you should hear it, because it will show you what a terrible calamity the smallpox was to our forefathers. The history of the province, (and, of course, the history of our chair,) would be incomplete without particular mention of it." Accordingly, Grandfather told the children a story, to which, for want of a better title, we shall give that of

The Rejected Blessing

One day, in 1721, Doctor Cotton Mather sat in his library, reading a book that had been published by the Royal Society of London. But, every few moments, he laid the book upon the table and leaned back in Grandfather's chair with an aspect of deep care and disquietude. There were certain things which troubled him exceedingly, so that he could hardly fix his thoughts upon what he read.

It was now a gloomy time in Boston. That terrible disease, the smallpox, had recently made its appearance in the town. Ever since the first settlement of the country, this awful pestilence had come, at intervals, and swept away multitudes of the inhabitants. Whenever it commenced its ravages, nothing seemed to stay its progress, until there were no more victims for it to seize upon. Oftentimes, hundreds of people, at once, lay groaning with its agony; and when it departed, its deep footsteps were always to be traced in many graves.

The people never felt secure from this calamity. Sometimes, perhaps, it was brought into the country by a poor sailor, who had caught the infection in foreign parts, and came hither to die and to be the cause of many deaths. Sometimes, no doubt, it followed in the train of the pompous governors when they came over from England. Sometimes the disease lay hidden in the cargoes of ships, among silks, and brocades, and other costly merchandise, which was imported for the rich people to wear. And sometimes it started up seemingly of its own accord, and nobody could tell whence it came. The physician, being called to attend the sick person, would look at him and say, "It is the small pox! Let the patient be carried to the hospital."

And now, this dreadful sickness had shown itself again in Boston. Cotton Mather was greatly afflicted, for the sake of the whole province. He had children, too, who were exposed to the danger. At that very moment he heard the voice of his youngest son, for whom his heart was moved with apprehension.

"Alas! I fear for that poor child," said Cotton Mather to himself. "What shall I do for my son Samuel?"

Again, he attempted to drive away these thoughts by taking up the book which he had been reading. And now, all of a sudden, his attention became fixed. The book contained a printed letter that an Italian physician had written upon the very subject about which Cotton Mather was so anxiously meditating. He ran his eye eagerly over the pages; and, behold! A method was disclosed to him by which the small pox might be robbed of its worst terrors. Such a method was known in Greece. The physicians of Turkey, too, those long-bearded Eastern sages, had been acquainted with it for many years. The Negroes of Africa, ignorant as they were, had likewise practised it, and thus had shown themselves wiser than the white men.

"Of a truth," ejaculated Cotton Mather, clasping his hands and looking up to Heaven, "it was a merciful Providence that brought this book under mine eye! I will procure a consultation of physicians, and see whether this wondrous inoculation may not stay the progress of the Destroyer."

So he arose from Grandfather's chair and went out of the library. Near the door he met his son Samuel, who seemed downcast and out of spirits. The boy had heard, probably, that some of his playmates were taken ill with the smallpox. But, as his father looked cheerfully at him, Samuel took courage, trusting that either the wisdom of so learned a minister would find some remedy for the danger, or else that his prayers would secure protection from on high.

Meanwhile, Cotton Mather took his staff and three-cornered hat and walked about the streets, calling at the houses of all the physicians in Boston. They were a very wise fraternity; and their huge wigs, and black dresses, and solemn visages, made their wisdom appear even profounder than it was. One after another, he acquainted them with the discovery which he had hit upon.

But these grave and sagacious personages would scarcely listen to him. The oldest doctor in town contented himself with remarking that no such thing as inoculation was mentioned by Galen‡ or Hippocrates,‡ and it was impossible that modern physicians should be wiser than those old sages. A second held up his hands in dumb astonishment and horror at the madness of what Cotton Mather proposed to do. A third told him, in pretty plain terms, that he knew not what he was talking about. A fourth requested, in the name of the whole medical fraternity, that Cotton Mather would confine his attention to people's souls, and leave the physicians to take care of their bodies.

In short, there was but a single doctor among them all who would grant the poor minister so much as a patient hearing. This was Doctor Zabdiel Boylston. He looked into the matter like a man of sense, and finding, beyond a doubt, that inoculation had rescued many from death, he resolved to try the experiment in his own family.

And so he did. But, when the other physicians heard of it, they arose in great fury, and began a war of words, written, printed, and spoken, against Cotton Mather and Doctor Boylston. To hear them talk, you would have supposed that these two harmless and benevolent men had plotted the ruin of the country.

The people, also, took the alarm. Many, who thought themselves more pious than their neighbors, contended that, if Providence had ordained them to die of the smallpox, it was sinful to aim at preventing it. The strangest reports were in circulation. Some said that Doctor Boylston had contrived a method for conveying the gout, rheumatism, sick

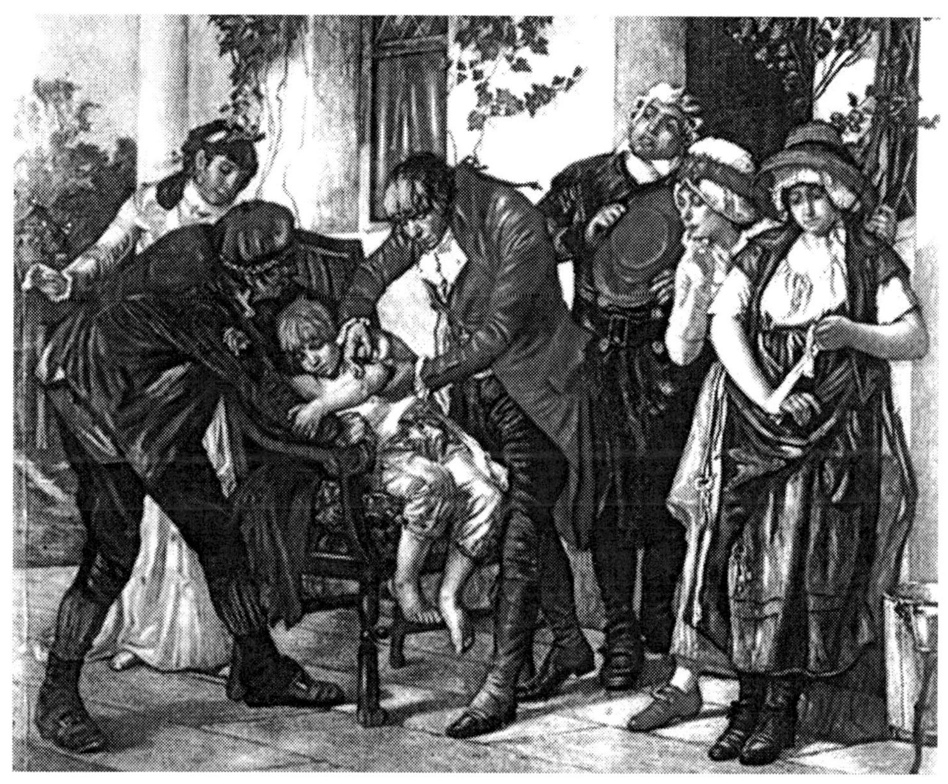

AN INOCULATION

headache, asthma, and all other diseases, from one person to another, and diffusing them through the whole community. Others flatly affirmed that the Evil One had got possession of Cotton Mather, and was at the bottom of the whole business.

You must observe, children, that Cotton Mather's fellow citizens were generally inclined to doubt the wisdom of any measure, which he might propose to them. They recollected how he had led them astray in the old witchcraft delusion; and now, if he thought and acted ever so wisely, it was difficult for him to get the credit of it.

The people's wrath grew so hot at his attempt to guard them from the smallpox, that he could not walk the streets in peace. Whenever the venerable form of the old minister, meagre and haggard with fasts and vigils, was seen approach-

FEARS OF THE EFFECTS OF VACCINATION

ing, hisses were heard, and shouts of derision, and scornful and bitter laughter. The women snatched away their children from his path, lest he should do them a mischief. Still, however, bending his head meekly, and perhaps stretching out his hands to bless those who reviled him, he pursued his way. But the tears came into his eyes, to think how blindly the people rejected the means of safety that were offered them.

Indeed, there were melancholy sights enough in the streets of Boston, to draw forth the tears of a compassionate man. Over the door of almost every dwelling, a red flag was fluttering in the air. This was the signal that the smallpox had entered the house, and attacked some member of the family; or perhaps the whole family, old and young, were struggling at once with the pestilence. Friends and relatives, when they met one another in the streets, would hurry onward without a grasp of the hand, or scarcely a word of greeting, lest they should catch or communicate the contagion. And, often a coffin was borne hastily along.

"Alas, alas!" said Cotton Mather to himself. "What shall be done for this poor, misguided people? Oh, that Providence would open their eyes, and enable them to discern good from evil!"

So furious, however, were the people, that they threatened vengeance against any person who should dare to practise inoculation, though it were only in his own family. This was a hard case for Cotton Mather, who saw no other way to rescue his poor child Samuel from the disease. But he resolved to save him, even if his house should be burnt over his head.

"I will not be turned aside," said he. "My townsmen shall see that I have faith in this thing, when I make the experiment on my beloved son,‡ whose life is dearer to me than my own. And when I have saved Samuel, peradventure they will be persuaded to save themselves."

Accordingly, Samuel was inoculated; and so was Mr. Walter, a son-in-law of Cotton Mather. Doctor Boylston, likewise, inoculated many persons; and while hundreds died, who had caught the contagion from the garments of the sick, almost all were preserved, who followed the wise physician's advice.‡

But the people were not yet convinced of their mistake. One night, a destructive little instrument, called a hand grenade,‡ was thrown into Cotton Mather's window, and rolled under Grandfather's chair. It was supposed to be filled with gunpowder, the explosion of which would have blown the poor minister to atoms. But the best informed historians are of opinion that the grenade contained only brimstone and asafetida, and was meant to plague Cotton Mather with a very evil perfume.

This is no strange thing in human experience. Men, who attempt to do the world more good than the world is able entirely to comprehend, are almost invariably held in bad odor. But yet, if the wise and good man can wait awhile, either the present generation or posterity, will do him justice. So it proved, in the case which we have been speaking of. In after years, when inoculation was universally practised, and thousands were saved from death by it, the people remembered old Cotton Mather, then sleeping in his grave. They acknowledged that the very thing, for which they had so reviled and persecuted him, was the best and wisest thing he ever did.

***

"Grandfather, this is not an agreeable story," observed Clara.

"No, Clara," replied Grandfather. "But it is right that you should know what a dark shadow this disease threw over the times of our forefathers. And now, if you wish to learn more about Cotton Mather, you must read his biography, written by Mr. Peabody,‡ of Springfield. You will find it very entertaining and instructive; but perhaps the writer is somewhat too harsh in his judgment of this singular man. He estimates him fairly, indeed, and understands him well; but he unriddles his character rather by acuteness than by sympathy. Now, his life should have been written by one, who, knowing all his faults, would nevertheless love him."

So Grandfather made an end of Cotton Mather, telling his auditors that he died in 1728, at the age of sixty-five, and bequeathed the chair to Elisha Cooke.‡ This gentleman was a famous advocate of the people's rights.

The same year, William Burnet, a son of the celebrated Bishop Burnet, arrived in Boston, with the commission of governor. He was the first that had been appointed since the departure of Colonel Shute. Gover-

MATHER'S VAULT

nor Burnet took up his residence with Mr. Cooke, while the Province House was undergoing repairs. During this period, he was always complimented with a seat in Grandfather's chair; and so comfortable did he find it, that on removing to the Province House, he could not bear to leave it behind him. Mr. Cooke, therefore, requested his acceptance of it.

"I should think," said Laurence, "that the people would have petitioned the king always to appoint a native born New Englander to govern them."

"Undoubtedly it was a grievance," answered Grandfather, "to see men placed in this station, who perhaps had neither talents nor virtues to fit them for it, and who certainly could have no natural affection for the country. The king generally bestowed the governorships of the American colonies upon needy noblemen, or hangers-on at court, or disbanded officers. The people knew that such persons would be very likely to make the good of the country subservient to the wishes of the king. The legislature, therefore, endeavored to keep as much power as possible in their own hands, by refusing to settle a fixed salary upon the governors. It was thought better to pay them according to their deserts."

"Did Governor Burnet work well for his money?" asked Charley.

Grandfather could not help smiling at the simplicity of Charley's question. Nevertheless, it put the matter in a very plain point of view.

He then described the character of Governor Burnet, representing him as a good scholar, possessed of much ability, and likewise of unspotted integrity. His story affords a striking example, how unfortunate it is for a man, who is placed as ruler over a country, to be compelled to aim at any thing but the good of the people. Governor Burnet was so chained down by his instructions from the king, that he could not act as he might otherwise have wished. Consequently, his whole term of office was wasted in quarrels with the legislature.

"I am afraid, children," said Grandfather, "that Governor Burnet found but little rest or comfort in our old chair. Here he used to sit, dressed in a coat which was made of rough, shaggy cloth outside, but of smooth velvet within. It was said that his own character resembled that coat, for his outward manner was rough, but his inward disposition soft and kind. It is a pity that such a man could not have been kept free from trouble. But so harassing were his disputes with the representatives of the people, that he fell into a fever, of which he died, in 1720. The legislature had refused him a salary, while alive; but they appropriated money enough to give him a splendid and pompous funeral."

And now Grandfather perceived that little Alice had fallen fast asleep, with her head upon his footstool. Indeed, as Clara observed, she had been sleeping from the time of Sir Hovenden Walker's expedition against Quebec, until the death of Governor Burnet–a period of about eighteen years. And yet, after so long a nap, sweet little Alice was a golden-haired child, of scarcely five years old.

"It puts me in mind," said Laurence, "of the story of the enchanted princess, who slept many a hundred years, and awoke as young and beautiful as ever."

Chapter VI
Pomps and Vanities

A few evenings afterwards, cousin Clara happened to inquire of Grandfather, whether the old chair had never been present at a ball. At the same time, little Alice brought forward a doll, with whom she had been holding a long conversation.

"See, Grandfather," cried she. "Did such a pretty lady as this ever sit in your great chair?"

These questions led Grandfather to talk about the fashions and manners, which now began to be introduced from England into the provinces. The simplicity of the good old Puritan times was fast disappearing. This was partly owing to the increasing number and wealth of the inhabitants, and to the additions which they continually received, by the arrival and settlement of people from beyond the sea.

Another cause of a pompous and artificial mode of life, among those who could afford it, was that the example was set by the royal governors. Under the old charter, the governors were the representatives of the people, and therefore their way of living had probably been marked by a popular simplicity. But now, as they represented the person of the king, they thought it necessary to preserve the dignity of their station by the practice of high and gorgeous ceremonials. And, besides, the profitable offices under the government were filled by men who had lived in London, and had there contracted fashionable and luxurious habits of living, which they would not now lay aside. The wealthy people of the province imitated them; and thus began a general change in social life.

"So, my dear Clara," said Grandfather, "after our chair had entered the Province House,‡ it must often have been present at balls and festivals, though I cannot give you a description of any particular one. But I doubt not that they were very magnificent; and slaves in gorgeous liveries† waited on the guests, and offered them wine in goblets of massive silver."

"Were there slaves in those days?" exclaimed Clara.

"Yes; black slaves and white," replied Grandfather. "Our ancestors not only brought Negroes from Africa, but Indians from South America, and white people from Ireland. These last were sold, not for life, but for a certain number of years, in order to pay the expenses of their voyage across the Atlantic. Nothing was more common than to see a lot of likely Irish girls‡ advertised for sale in the newspapers. As for the little Negro babies,‡ they were offered to be given away, like young kittens."

"Perhaps Alice would have liked one to play with, instead of her doll," said Charley, laughing.

But little Alice clasped the waxen doll closer to her bosom.

"Now, as for this pretty doll, my little Alice," said Grandfather, "I wish you could have seen what splendid dresses the ladies wore in those times. They had silks, and satins, and damasks, and brocades, and high headdresses, and all sorts of fine things. And they used to wear hooped petticoats, of such enormous size that it was quite a journey to walk round them."

"And how did the gentlemen dress?" asked Charley.

"With full as much magnificence as the ladies," answered Grandfather. "For their holiday suits, they had coats of figured velvet, crimson, green, blue, and all other gay colors, embroidered with gold or silver lace. Their waistcoats, which were five times as large as modern ones, were very splendid. Sometimes, the whole waistcoat, which came down almost to the knees, was made of gold brocade."

"Why, the wearer must have shone like a golden image!" said Clara.

HIGH FASHION

"And, then," continued Grandfather, "they wore various sorts of periwigs,‡ such as the Tie, the Spencer, the Brigadier, the Major, the Albemarle, the Ramilies, the Feather-top, and the Full-bottom! Their three-cornered hats were laced with gold or silver. They had shining buckles at the knees of their smallclothes, and buckles likewise in their shoes. They wore swords, with beautiful hilts, either of silver, or sometimes of polished steel, inlaid with gold."

"Oh, I should like to wear a sword!" cried Charley.

"And an embroidered crimson velvet coat," said Clara, laughing, "and a gold brocade waistcoat down to your knees!"

"And knee-buckles and shoe-buckles," said Laurence, laughing also.

"And a periwig," added little Alice, soberly, not knowing what was the article of dress, which she recommended to our friend Charley.

Grandfather smiled at the idea of Charley's sturdy little figure in such a grotesque caparison†. He then went on with the history of the chair, and told the children, that in 1730, King George the Second appointed Jonathan Belcher to be governor of Massachusetts, in place of the deceased Governor Burnet. Mr. Belcher was a native of the province, but had spent much of his life in Europe.

The new governor found Grandfather's chair in the Province House, he was struck with its noble and stately aspect, but was of opinion that age and hard services had made it scarcely so fit for courtly company, as when it stood in the Earl of Lincoln's hall. Wherefore, as Governor Belcher was fond of splendor, he employed a skillful artist to beautify the chair. This was done by polishing and varnishing it, and by gilding the carved work of the elbows, and likewise the oaken flowers of the back. The lion's head now shone like a veritable lump of gold. Finally, Governor Belcher‡ gave the chair a cushion of blue damask, with a rich golden fringe.

"Our good old chair being thus glorified," proceeded Grandfather, "it glittered with a great deal more splendor than it had exhibited just a century before, when the Lady Arbella brought it over from England. Most people mistook it for a chair of the latest London fashion. And this may serve for an example that there is almost always an old and timeworn substance under all the glittering show of new invention."

"Grandfather, I cannot see any of the gilding," remarked Charley, who had been examining the chair very minutely.

"You will not wonder that it has been rubbed off," replied Grandfather, "when you hear all the adventures that have since befallen the chair. Gilded it was; and the handsomest room in the Province House was adorned by it."

There was not much to interest the children, in what happened during the years that Governor Belcher remained in the chair. At first, like Colonel Shute and Governor Burnet, he was engaged in disputing with the legislature about his salary. But, as he found it impossible to get a fixed sum, he finally obtained the king's leave to accept whatever the legislature chose to give him. And thus the people triumphed, after this long contest for the privilege of expending their own money as they saw fit.

The remainder of Governor Belcher's term of office was principally taken up in endeavoring to settle the currency.

Honest John Hull's pine tree shillings had long ago been worn out, or lost, or melted down again, and their place was supplied by bills of paper or parchment, which were nominally valued at three pence and upwards. The value of these bills kept continually sinking, because the real hard money could not be obtained for them. They were a great deal worse than the old Indian currency of clamshells. These disorders of the circulating medium were a source of endless plague and perplexity to the rulers and legislators, not only in Governor Belcher's days, but for many years before and afterwards.

Finally, the people suspected that Governor Belcher was secretly endeavoring to establish the Episcopal mode of worship in the provinces. There was enough of the old Puritan spirit remaining, to cause most of the true sons of New England to look with horror upon such an attempt. Great exertions were made to induce the king to remove the governor. Accordingly, in 1740, he was compelled to resign his office, and Grandfather's chair into the bargain, to Mr. Shirley.

Chapter VII
The Provincial Muster

"William Shirley," said Grandfather, "had come from England a few years before, and begun to practise law in Boston. You will think, perhaps, that as he had been a lawyer, the new governor used to sit in our great chair, reading heavy law books from morning till night. On the contrary, he was as stirring and active a governor as Massachusetts ever had. Even Sir William Phips hardly equalled him. The first year or two of his administration was spent in trying to regulate the currency. But, in 1744, after a peace of more than thirty years, war broke out between France and England."

"And I suppose," said Charley, "the governor went to take Canada."

"Not exactly, Charley," said Grandfather, "though you have made a pretty shrewd conjecture. He planned, in 1745, an expedition against Louisbourg. This was a fortified city, on the Island of Cape Breton, near Nova Scotia. Its walls were of immense height and strength, and were defended by hundreds of heavy cannon. It was the strongest fortress which the French possessed in America‡; and if the king of France had guessed Governor Shirley's intentions, he would have sent all the ships he could muster, to protect it."

As the siege of Louisbourg was one of the most remarkable events that ever the inhabitants of New England were engaged in, Grandfather endeavored to give his auditors a lively idea of the spirit with which they set about it. We shall call his description

The Provincial Muster

The expedition against Louisbourg first began to be thought of in the month of January. From that time, the governor's chair was continually surrounded by counsellors, representatives, clergymen, captains, pilots, and all manner of people, with whom he consulted about this wonderful project.

First of all, it was necessary to provide men and arms. The legislature immediately sent out a huge quantity of paper money, with which, as if by magic spell, the governor hoped to get possession of all the old cannon, powder and balls, rusty swords and muskets, and every thing else that would be serviceable in killing Frenchmen. Drums were beaten in all the villages of Massachusetts, to enlist soldiers for the service. Messages were sent to the other governors of New England, and to New York and Pennsylvania, entreating them to unite in this crusade against the French. All these provinces agreed to give what assistance they could.

But there was one very important thing to be decided. Who shall be the general of this great army? Peace had continued such an unusual length of time, that there was now less military experience among the colonists, than at any former period. The old Puritans had always kept their weapons bright, and were never destitute of warlike captains, who were skillful in assault or defense. But the swords of their descendants had grown rusty by disuse. There was nobody in New England that knew any thing about sieges, or any other regular fighting. The only persons, at all acquainted with warlike business, were a few elderly men, who had hunted Indians through the underbrush of the forest, in old Governor Dummer's war.

In this dilemma, Governor Shirley fixed upon a wealthy merchant, named William Pepperell,‡ who was pretty well known and liked among the people. As to military skill, he had no more of it than his neighbors. But, as the governor urged him very pressingly, Mr. Pepperell consented to shut up his leger, gird on a sword, and assume the title of General.

Meantime, what a hubbub was raised by this scheme! Rub-a-dub-dub! Rub-a-dub-dub! The rattle of drums, beat-

PEPPERELL AT LOUISBOURG

en out of all manner of time, was heard above every other sound.

Nothing now was so valuable as arms, of whatever style and fashion they might be. The bellows blew, and the hammer clanged continually upon the anvil, while the blacksmiths were repairing the broken weapons of other wars. Doubtless, some of the soldiers lugged out those enormous, heavy muskets, which used to be fired with rests,‡ in the time of the early Puritans. Great horse pistols, too, were found, which would go off with a bang like a cannon. Old cannon, with touch-holes† almost as big as their muzzles, were looked upon as inestimable treasures. Pikes, which perhaps, had been handled by Miles Standish's soldiers, now made their appearance again. Many a young man ransacked the garret,† and brought forth his great-grandfather's sword, corroded with rust, and stained with the blood of King Philip's war.

Never had there been seen such an arming as this, when a people, so long peaceful, rose to the war, with the best weapons that they could lay their hands upon. And still the drums were heard–Rub-a-dub-dub! Rub-a-dub-dub!–in all the towns and villages; and louder and more numerous grew the trampling footsteps of the recruits that marched behind.

And now the army began to gather into Boston. Tall, lanky, awkward, fellows, came in squads, and companies, and regiments, swaggering along, dressed in their brown homespun clothes and blue yarn stockings. They stooped, as if they still had hold of the plough handles, and marched without any time or tune. Hither they came, from the cornfields, from the clearing in the forest, from the blacksmith's forge, from the carpenter's workshop, and from the shoemaker's seat. They were an army of rough faces and sturdy frames. A trained officer of Europe would have laughed at them, till his sides had ached. But there was a spirit in their bosoms, which is more essential to soldiership than to wear red coats, and march in stately ranks to the sound of regular music.

Still was heard the beat of the drum–rub-a-dub-dub!–and now a host of three or four thousand men had found their way to Boston. Little quiet was there then! Forth scampered the schoolboys, shouting behind the drums. The whole town–the whole land–was on fire with war.

After the arrival of the troops, they were probably reviewed upon the Common†. We may imagine Governor Shirley and General Pepperell riding slowly along the line, while the drummers beat strange old tunes, like psalm tunes, and all the officers and soldiers put on their most warlike looks. It would have been a terrible sight for the Frenchmen, could they but have witnessed it!

At length, on the twenty-fourth of March, 1745, the army gave a parting shout, and set sail from Boston in ten or twelve vessels, which had been hired by the governor. A few days afterwards, an English fleet, commanded by Commodore Peter Warren, sailed also for Louisbourg, to assist the provincial army. So, now, after all this bustle of preparation, the town and province were left in stillness and repose.

But, stillness and repose, at such a time of anxious expectation, are hard to bear. The hearts of the old people and women sunk within them, when they reflected what perils they had sent their sons, and husbands, and brothers, to encounter. The

TO ARMS! TO ARMS!

boys loitered heavily to school, missing the rub-a-dub-dub, and the trampling march, in the rear of which they had so lately run and shouted. All the ministers prayed earnestly, in their pulpits, for a blessing on the army of New England. In every family, when the good man lifted up his heart in domestic worship, the burden of his petition was for the safety of those dear ones, who were fighting under the walls of Louisbourg.

Governor Shirley, all this time, was probably in an ecstasy of impatience. He could not sit still a moment. He found no quiet, not even in Grandfather's chair, but hurried to-and-fro, and up and down the staircase of the Province House. Now, he mounted to the cupola,† and looked seaward, straining his eyes to discover if there were a sail upon the horizon. Now, he hastened down the stairs, and stood beneath the portal, on the red freestone steps, to receive some mud-bespattered courtier, from whom he hoped to hear tidings of the army.

A few weeks after the departure of the troops, Commodore Warren sent a small vessel to Boston, with two French prisoners. One of them was Monsieur Bouladrie, who had been commander of a battery, outside of the walls of Louisbourg. The other was the Marquis de la Maison Forte, captain of a French frigate, which had been taken by Commodore Warren's fleet. These prisoners assured Governor Shirley that the fortifications of Louisbourg were far too strong ever to be stormed by the provincial army.

Day after day, and week after week, went on. The people

grew almost heartsick with anxiety; for the flower of the country was at peril in this adventurous expedition. It was now daybreak, on the morning of the third of July.

But, hark! What sound is this? The hurried clang of a bell! There is the Old North, pealing suddenly out! There, the Old South strikes in! Now, the peal comes from the church in Brattle Street! The bells of nine or ten steeples are all flinging their iron voices, at once, upon the morning breeze! Is it joy or alarm? There goes the roar of a cannon, too! A royal salute is thundered forth. And, now, we hear the loud exulting shout of a multitude, assembled in the street. Huzza, Huzza! Louisbourg has surrendered![‡] Huzza!

***

"Oh Grandfather, how glad I should have been to live in those times!" cried Charley. "And what reward did the king give to General Pepperell and Governor Shirley?"

"He made Pepperell a baronet; so that he was now to be called Sir William Pepperell," replied Grandfather. "He likewise appointed both Pepperell and Shirley to be colonels in the royal army. These rewards, and higher ones, were well deserved; for this was the greatest triumph that the English met with, in the whole course of that war. General Pepperell became a man of great fame. I have seen a full length portrait of him, representing him in a splendid scarlet uniform, standing before the walls of Louisbourg, while several bombs are falling through the air."

"But, did the country gain any real good by the conquest of Louisbourg?" asked Laurence. "Or was all the benefit reaped by Pepperell and Shirley?"

"The English Parliament," said Grandfather, "agreed to pay the colonists for all the expenses of the siege. Accordingly, in 1749, two hundred and fifteen chests of Spanish dollars, and one hundred casks of copper coin, were brought from England to Boston. The whole amount was about a million dollars. Twenty-seven carts and trucks carried this money from the wharf to the provincial treasury. Was not this a pretty liberal reward?"

"The mothers of the young men, who were killed at the siege of Louisbourg, would not have thought it so," said Laurence.

"No, Laurence," rejoined Grandfather; "and every warlike achievement involves an amount of physical and moral evil, for which all the gold in the Spanish mines would not be the slightest recompense. But, we are to consider that this siege was one of the occasions, on which the colonists tested their ability for war, and thus were prepared for the great contest of the Revolution. In that point of view, the valor of our forefathers was its own reward."

Grandfather went on to say that the success of the expedition against Louisbourg induced Shirley and Pepperell to form a scheme for conquering Canada. This plan, however, was not carried into execution.

In the year 1746, great terror was excited by the arrival of a formidable French fleet upon the coast. It was commanded by the Duke d'Anville, and consisted of forty ships of war, besides vessels with soldiers on board. With this force, the French intended to retake Louisbourg, and afterwards to ravage the whole of New England. Many people were ready to give up the country for lost.

But the hostile fleet met with so many disasters and losses, by storm and shipwreck, that the Duke d'Anville‡ is said to have poisoned himself in despair. The officer next in command threw himself upon his sword and perished. Thus deprived of their commanders, the remainder of the ships returned to France. This was as great a deliverance for New England, as that which old England had experienced in the days of Queen Elizabeth, when the Spanish Armada‡ was wrecked upon her coast.

"In 1747," proceeded Grandfather, "Governor Shirley was driven from the Province House, not by a hostile fleet and army, but by a mob of the Boston people. They were so incensed at the conduct of the British Commodore Knowles, who had impressed† some of their fellow citizens, that several thousands of them surrounded the council chamber, and threw stones and brick-bats into the windows. The governor attempted to pacify them; but, not succeeding, he thought it necessary to leave the town, and take refuge within the walls of Castle William.‡ Quiet was not restored, until Commodore Knowles had sent back the impressed men. This affair was a flash of spirit that might have warned the English not to venture upon any oppressive measures against their colonial brethren."

Peace being declared between France and England in 1748, the governor had now an opportunity to sit at his ease in Grandfather's chair. Such repose, however, appears not to have suited his disposition; for, in the following year, he went to England, and thence was dispatched to France, on public business. Meanwhile, as Shirley had not resigned his office, Lieutenant-Governor Phips acted as chief magistrate in his stead.

Chapter VIII
The Old French War and the Acadian Exiles

In the early twilight of Thanksgiving eve, came Laurence, and Clara, and Charley, and little Alice, hand in hand, and stood in a semi-circle round Grandfather's chair. They had been joyous, throughout that day of festivity, mingling together in all kinds of play, so that the house had echoed with their airy mirth.

Grandfather, too, had been happy, though not mirthful. He felt that this was to be set down as one of the good Thanksgivings of his life. In truth, all his former Thanksgivings had borne their part in the present one; for, his years of infancy, and youth, and manhood with their blessings and their griefs, had flitted before him, while he sat silently in the great chair. Vanished scenes had been pictured in the air. The forms of departed friends had visited him. Voices, to be heard no more on earth, had sent an echo from the infinite and the eternal. These shadows, if such they were, seemed almost as real to him, as what was actually present–as the merry shouts and laughter of the children–as their figures, dancing like sunshine before his eyes.

He felt that the past was not taken from him. The happiness of former days was a possession forever. And there was something in the mingled sorrow of his lifetime that became akin to happiness, after being long treasured in the depths of his heart. There it underwent a change, and grew more precious than pure gold.

And now came the children, somewhat aweary with their wild play, and sought the quiet enjoyment of Grandfather's talk. The good old gentleman rubbed his eyes, and smiled round upon them all. He was glad, as most aged people are, to find that he was yet of consequence, and could give pleasure to the world. After being so merry, all day long, did these children desire to hear his sober talk? Oh, then, old Grandfather had yet a place to fill among living men,–or at least among boys and girls!

"Begin quick, Grandfather," cried little Alice; "for Pussy wants to hear you."

And, truly, our yellow friend, the cat, lay upon the hearth rug, basking in the warmth of the fire, pricking up her ears, and turning her head from the children to Grandfather, and from Grandfather to the children, as if she felt herself very sympathetic with them all. A loud purr, like the singing of a tea kettle, or the hum of a spinning-wheel, testified that she was as comfortable and happy as a cat could be. For Puss had feasted, and therefore, like Grandfather and the children, had kept a good Thanksgiving.

"Does Pussy want to hear me?" said Grandfather, smiling. "Well; we must please Pussy, if we can!"

And so he took up the history of the chair, from the epoch of the peace of 1748. By one of the provisions of the treaty, Louisbourg, which the New Englanders had been at so much pains to take, was restored to the king of France.

The French were afraid that unless their colonies should be better defended than heretofore, another war might deprive them of the whole. Almost as soon as peace was declared, therefore, they began to build strong fortifications in the interior of North America. It was strange to behold these warlike castles, on the banks of solitary lakes, and far in the midst of woods. The Indian, paddling his birch canoe on Lake Champlain, looked up at the high ramparts of Ticonderoga, stone piled on stone, bristling with cannon, and the white flag of France floating above. There were similar fortifications on Lake Ontario, and near the great Falls of Niagara, and at the sources of the Ohio River. And all around these forts and castles lay the eternal forest; and the roll of the drum died away in those deep solitudes.

The truth was that the French intended to build forts, all the way from Canada to Louisiana. They would then have had a wall of military strength, at the back of the English settlements, so as completely to hem them in. The king of England considered the building of these forts as a sufficient cause of war, which was accordingly commenced in 1754.

"Governor Shirley," said Grandfather, "had returned to Boston in 1753. While in Paris, he had married a second wife, a young French girl, and now brought her to the Province House. But, when war was breaking out, it was impossible for such a bustling man to stay quietly at home, sitting in our old chair, with his wife and children round about him. He therefore obtained a command in the English forces."

"And what did Sir William Pepperell do?" asked Charley.

"He stayed at home," said Grandfather, "and was general of the militia. The veteran regiments of the English army, which were now sent across the Atlantic, would have scorned to fight under the orders of an old American merchant. And now began what aged people call the Old French War. It would be going too far astray from the history of our chair, to tell you one-half of the battles that were fought. I cannot even allow myself to describe the bloody defeat of General Braddock,‡ near the sources of the Ohio River, in 1755. But, I must not omit to mention that when the English general was mortally wounded, and his army routed, the remains of it were preserved by the skill and valor of George Washington."‡

At the mention of this illustrious name, the children started, as if a sudden sunlight had gleamed upon the history of their country, now that the great Deliverer had arisen above the horizon.

Among all the events of the Old French War, Grandfather thought that there was none more interesting than the removal of the inhabitants of Acadia. From the first settle-

STONE FORT

ment of this ancient province of the French, in 1604, until the present time, its people could scarcely ever know what kingdom held dominion over them. They were a peaceful race, taking no delight in warfare, and caring nothing for military renown. And yet, in every war, their region was infested with iron-hearted soldiers, both French and English, who fought one another for the privilege of ill-treating these poor harmless Acadians. Sometimes the treaty of peace made them subjects of one king, sometimes of another.

At the peace of 1748, Acadia had been ceded to England. But the French still claimed a large portion of it, and built forts for its defense. In 1755, these forts were taken, and the whole of Acadia was conquered by three thousand men from Massachusetts, under the command of General Winslow. The inhabitants were accused of supplying the French with provisions, and of doing other things that violated their neutrality.

"These accusations were probably true," observed Grandfather; "for the Acadians were descended from the French, and had the same friendly feelings towards them that the people of Massachusetts had for the English. But their punishment was severe. The English determined to tear these poor people from their native homes and scatter them abroad."

The Acadians were about seven thousand in number. A considerable part of them were made prisoners, and transported to the English colonies. All their dwellings and churches were burnt, their cattle were killed, and the whole country was laid waste, so that none of them might find shelter or food in their old homes after the departure of the

English. One thousand of the prisoners were sent to Massachusetts; and Grandfather allowed his fancy to follow them thither, and tried to give his auditors an idea of their situation.

We shall call this passage the story of

The Acadian Exiles

A sad day it was for the poor Acadians, when the armed soldiers drove them, at the point of the bayonet, down to the seashore. Very sad were they, likewise, while tossing upon the ocean, in the crowded transport vessels. But, methinks, it must have been sadder still, when they were landed on the Long Wharf, in Boston, and left to themselves, on a foreign strand.

Then, probably, they huddled together, and looked into one another's faces for the comfort which was not there. Hitherto, they had been confined on board of separate vessels, so that they could not tell whether their relatives and friends were prisoners along with them. But, now, at least, they could tell that many had been left behind, or transported to other regions.

Now, a desolate wife might be heard calling for her husband. He, alas! had gone, she knew not whither, or perhaps had fled into the woods of Acadia, and had now returned to weep over the ashes of their dwelling. An aged widow was crying out, in a querulous,† lamentable tone, for her son, whose affectionate toil had supported her for many a year. He was not in the crowd of exiles†; and what could this aged widow do but sink down and die? Young men and

EMBARKING ACADIAN EXILES

maidens, whose hearts had been torn asunder by separation, had hoped, during the voyage, to meet their beloved ones at its close. Now, they began to feel that they were separated forever. And, perhaps, a lonesome little girl, a golden-haired child of five years old, the very picture of our little Alice, was weeping and wailing for her mother, and found not a soul to give her a kind word.

Oh, how many broken bonds of affection were here! Country lost!–friends lost!–their rural wealth of cottage, field, and herds, all lost together! Every tie between these poor exiles and the world seemed to be cut off at once. They must have regretted that they had not died before their exile; for even the English would not have been so pitiless as to deny them graves in their native soil. The dead were happy; for they were not exiles!

While they thus stood upon the wharf, the curiosity and inquisitiveness of the New England people would naturally lead them into the midst of the poor Acadians. Prying busybodies thrust their heads into the circle, wherever two or three of the exiles were conversing together. How puzzled did they look, at the outlandish sound of the French tongue! There were seen the New England women, too. They had just come out of their warm, safe homes, where every thing was regular and comfortable, and where their husbands and children would be with them at nightfall. Surely, they could pity the wretched wives and mothers of Acadia! Or, did the sign of the cross, which the Acadians continually made upon their breasts, and which was abhorred by the descendants of the Puritans–did that sign exclude all pity?

Among the spectators, too, was the noisy brood of Boston schoolboys, who came running, with laughter and shouts, to gaze at this crowd of oddly dressed foreigners. At first they danced and capered around them, full of merriment and mischief. But the despair of the Acadians soon had its effect upon these thoughtless lads, and melted them into tearful sympathy.

At a little distance from the throng, might be seen the wealthy and pompous merchants, whose warehouses stood on Long Wharf. It was difficult to touch these rich men's hearts; for they had all the comforts of the world at their command; and when they walked abroad, their feelings were seldom moved, except by the roughness of the pavement, irritating their gouty toes. Leaning upon their gold-headed canes, they watched the scene with an aspect of composure. But, let us hope, they distributed some of their superfluous coin among these hapless exiles, to purchase food and a night's lodging.

After standing a long time at the end of the wharf, gazing seaward, as if to catch a glimpse of their lost Acadia, the strangers began to stray into the town.

They went, we will suppose, in parties and groups, here a hundred, there a score, there ten, there three or four, who possessed some bond of unity among themselves. Here and there was one, who, utterly desolate, stole away by himself, seeking no companionship.

Whither did they go? I imagine them wandering about the streets, telling the townspeople, in outlandish, unintelligible words, that no earthly affliction ever equaled what had befallen them. Man's brotherhood with man was sufficient to make the New Englanders understand this language. The strangers wanted food. Some of them sought hospitality at the doors of the stately mansions, which then stood in the vicinity of Hanover Street and the North Square. Others were applicants at the humble wooden tenements, where dwelt the petty shopkeepers and mechanics. Pray Heaven, that no family in Boston turned one of these poor exiles from their door! It would be a reproach upon New England–a crime worthy of heavy retribution–if the aged women and children, or even the strong men, were allowed to feel the pinch of hunger.

Perhaps some of the Acadians, in their aimless wanderings through the town, found themselves near a large brick edifice,† which was fenced in from the street by an iron railing, wrought with fantastic figures. They saw a flight of red freestone steps, ascending to a portal, above which was a balcony and balustrade†. Misery and desolation give men the right of free passage everywhere. Let us suppose, then, that they mounted the flight of steps, and passed into the Province House. Making their way into one of the apartments, they beheld a richly clad gentleman, seated in a stately chair, with gilding upon the carved work of its back, and a gilded lion's head at the summit. This was Governor Shirley, meditating upon matters of war and state, in Grandfather's chair!

If such an incident did happen, Shirley, reflecting what a ruin of peaceful and humble hopes had been wrought by the cold policy of the statesman, and the iron hand of the warrior, might have drawn a deep moral from it. It should have taught him that the poor man's hearth is sacred, and that armies and nations have no right to violate it. It should have made him feel that England's triumph, and increased dominion, could not compensate to mankind, nor atone to Heaven, for the ashes of a single Acadian cottage. But it is not thus that statesmen and warriors moralize.

"Grandfather," cried Laurence, with emotion trembling in his voice, "did iron-hearted War itself ever do so hard and cruel a thing as this before?"

"You have read in history, Laurence, of whole regions wantonly laid waste," said Grandfather. "In the removal of the Acadians, the troops were guilty of no cruelty or outrage, except what was inseparable from the measure."

Little Alice, whose eyes had, all along, been brimming full of tears, now burst forth a-sobbing; for Grandfather had touched her sympathies more than he intended.

"To think of a whole people, homeless in the world!" said Clara, with moistened eyes. "There never was any thing so sad!"

"It was their own fault," cried Charley, energetically. "Why did not they fight for the country where they were born? Then, if the worst had happened to them they could only have been killed and buried there. They would not have been exiles then!"

"Certainly, their lot was as hard as death," said Grandfather. "All that could be done for them, in the English provinces, was to send them to the almshouses, or bind them out to taskmasters. And this was the fate of persons, who had possessed a comfortable property in their native country. Some of them found means to embark for France; but though it was the land of their forefathers, it must have been a foreign land to them. Those, who remained behind, always cherished a belief that the king of France would never make peace with England, till his poor Acadians were restored their country and their homes."

"And did he?" inquired Clara.

"Alas, my dear Clara," said Grandfather, "it is improbable that the slightest whisper of the woes of Acadia ever reached the ears of Louis the Fifteenth. The exiles grew old in the British provinces, and never saw Acadia again. Their descendants remain among us, to this day. They have forgotten the language of their ancestors, and probably retain no tradition of their misfortunes. But, methinks, if I were an American poet, I would choose Acadia for the subject of my song."

Since Grandfather first spoke these words, the most famous of American poets has drawn sweet tears from all of us, by his beautiful poem of "Evangeline".‡

And now, having thrown a gentle gloom around the Thanksgiving fireside, by a story that made the children feel the blessing of a secure and peaceful hearth, Grandfather put off the other events of the Old French War till the next evening.

Chapter IX
The End of the War

In the twilight of the succeeding eve, when the red beams of the fire were dancing upon the wall, the children besought Grandfather to tell them what had next happened to the old chair.

"Our chair," said Grandfather, "stood all this time in the Province House. But, Governor Shirley had seldom an opportunity to repose within its arms. He was loading his troops through the forest, or sailing in a flatboat on Lake Ontario, or sleeping in his tent, while the awful cataract of Niagara sent its roar through his dreams. At one period, in the early part of the war, Shirley had the chief command of all the king's forces in America."

"Did his young wife go with him to the war?" asked Clara.

"I rather imagine," replied Grandfather, "that she remained in Boston. This lady, I suppose, had our chair all to herself, and used to sit in it, during those brief intervals when a young French woman can be quiet enough to sit in a chair. The people of Massachusetts were never fond of Governor Shirley's young French wife. They had a suspicion that she betrayed the military plans of the English to the generals of the French armies."

"And was it true?" inquired Clara.

"Probably not," said Grandfather. "But the mere suspicion did Shirley a great deal of harm. Partly, perhaps, for this reason, but much more on account of his inefficiency as a general, he was deprived of his command, in 1756, and recalled to England. He never afterwards made any figure in public life."

As Grandfather's chair had no locomotive properties, and did not even run on castors, it cannot be supposed to have marched in person to the Old French War. But Grandfather delayed its momentous history, while he touched briefly upon some of the bloody battles, sieges, and onslaughts, the tidings of which kept continually coming to the ears of the old inhabitants of Boston. The woods of the north were populous with fighting men. All the Indian tribes uplifted their tomahawks, and took part either with the French or English. The rattle of musketry and roar of cannon disturbed the ancient quiet of the forest, and actually drove the bears and other wild beasts to the more cultivated portion of the country in the vicinity of the seaports. The children felt as if they were transported back to those forgotten times, and that the couriers from the army,‡ with the news of a battle lost or won, might even now be heard galloping through the streets. Grandfather told them about the battle of Lake George, in 1755, when the gallant Colonel Williams,‡ a Massachusetts officer, was slain, with many of his countrymen. But General Johnson and General Lyman, with their army, drove back the enemy, and mortally wounded the French leader, who was called the Baron Dieskau.‡ A gold watch, pilfered from the poor Baron, is still in existence, and still marks each moment of time, without complaining of weariness, although its hands have been in motion ever since the hour of battle.

In the first years of the war, there were many disasters on the English side. Among these was the loss of Fort Oswego, in 1756, and of Fort William Henry, in the following year. But the greatest misfortune that befell the English, during the whole war, was the repulse of General Abercrombie,‡ with his army, from the ramparts of Ticonderoga, in 1758. He attempted to storm the walls; but a terrible conflict ensued, in which more than two thousand Englishmen and New Englanders were killed or wounded. The slain soldiers now lie buried around that ancient fortress. When the plough passes over the soil, it turns up here and there a moldering bone.

Up to this period, none of the English generals had shown any military talent. Shirley, the Earl of Loudon, and General Abercrombie, had each held the chief command, at different times; but not one of them had won a single important triumph for the British arms. This ill success‡ was not owing to the want of means; for, in 1758, General Abercrombie had fifty thousand soldiers under his command. But the French general, the famous Marquis de Montcalm,‡ possessed a great genius for war, and had something within him that taught him how battles were to be won.

At length, in 1759, Sir Jeffrey Amherst was appointed commander-in-chief of all the British forces in America. He was a man of ability, and a skillful soldier. A plan was now formed for accomplishing that object, which had so long been the darling wish of the New Englanders, and which their fathers had so many times attempted. This was the conquest of Canada.

Three separate armies were to enter Canada, from different quarters. One of the three, commanded by General Prideaux, was to embark on Lake Ontario, and proceed to Montreal. The second, at the head of which was Sir Jeffrey Amherst himself, was destined to reach the River St. Lawrence, by the way of Lake Champlain, and then go down the river to meet the third army. This last, led by General Wolfe, was to enter the St. Lawrence from the sea, and ascend the river to Quebec. It is to Wolfe and his army that England owes one of the most splendid triumphs, ever written in her history.

Grandfather described the siege of Quebec, and told how Wolfe led his soldiers up a rugged and lofty precipice that rose from the shore of the river to the plain on which the city stood. This bold adventure was achieved in the darkness of night. At daybreak, tidings were carried to the Marquis de Montcalm that the English army was waiting to give him battle on the plains of Abraham. This brave French general ordered his drums to strike up, and immediately marched to encounter Wolfe.

He marched to his own death. The battle was the most fierce and terrible that had ever been fought in America. General Wolfe was at the head of his soldiers, and while encouraging them onward, received a mortal wound. He reclined against a stone, in the agonies of death; but it seemed as if his spirit could not pass away, while the fight yet raged so doubtfully. Suddenly, a shout came pealing across the battlefield–"They flee! They flee!" And, for a moment, Wolfe lifted his languid head. "Who flee?" he inquired. "The French," replied an officer. "Then I die satisfied!" said Wolfe, and expired in the arms of victory.

"If ever a warrior's death were glorious, Wolfe's was so!" said Grandfather; and his eye kindled, though he was a man of peaceful thoughts, and gentle spirit. "His life-blood streamed to baptize the soil which he had added to the dominion of Britain! His dying breath was mingled with his army's shout of victory!"

"Oh, it was a good death to die!" cried Charley, with glistening eyes. "Was it not a good death, Laurence?"

Laurence made no reply; for his heart burned within him, as the picture of Wolfe,‡ dying on the bloodstained field of victory, arose to his imagination; and yet, he had a deep inward consciousness that, after all, there was a truer glory than could thus be won.

"There were other battles in Canada, after Wolfe's victory," resumed Grandfather; "but we may consider the Old French War as having terminated with this great event. The treaty of peace, however, was not signed until 1763. The terms of the treaty were very disadvantageous to the French; for all Canada, and all Acadia, and the island of Cape Breton, in short, all the territories that France and England had been fighting about, for nearly a hundred years–were surrendered to the English."

"So, now, at last," said Laurence, "New England had gained her wish. Canada was taken!"

"And now there was nobody to fight with, but the Indians," said Charley.

Grandfather mentioned two other important events. The first was the great fire of Boston,‡ in 1760, when the glare

DEATH OF GENERAL WOLFE

from nearly three hundred buildings, all in flames at once, shone through the windows of the Province House, and threw a fierce lustre upon the gilded foliage and lion's head of our old chair. The second event was the proclamation, in the same year, of George the Third as king of Great Britain. The blast of the trumpet sounded from the balcony of the Town House, and awoke the echoes far and wide, as if to challenge all mankind to dispute King George's title.

Seven times, as the successive monarchs of Britain ascended the throne, the trumpet peal of proclamation had been heard by those who sat in our venerable chair. But, when the next king put on his father's crown, no trumpet peal proclaimed it to New England! Long before that day, America had shaken off the royal government.

Chapter X

Thomas Hutchinson

Now that Grandfather had fought through the Old French War, in which our chair made no very distinguished figure, he thought it high time to tell the children some of the more private history of that praiseworthy old piece of furniture.

"In 1757," said Grandfather, "after Shirley had been summoned to England, Thomas Pownall was appointed governor of Massachusetts. He was a gay and fashionable English gentleman, who had spent much of his life in London, but had a considerable acquaintance with America. The new governor appears to have taken no active part in the war that was going on; although, at one period, he talked of marching against the enemy, at the head of his company of cadets. But, on the whole, he probably concluded that it was more befitting a governor to remain quietly in our chair, reading the newspapers and official documents."

"Did the people like Pownall?" asked Charley.

"They found no fault with him," replied Grandfather. "It was no time to quarrel with the governor, when the utmost harmony was required, in order to defend the country against the French. But Pownall did not remain long in Massachusetts. In 1759, he was sent to be governor of South Carolina. In thus exchanging one government for another, I suppose he felt no regret, except at the necessity of leaving Grandfather's chair behind him."

"He might have taken it to South Carolina," observed Clara.

"It appears to me," said Laurence, giving the rein to his fancy, "that the fate of this ancient chair was, somehow or other, mysteriously connected with the fortunes of old Massachusetts. If Governor Pownall had put it aboard the vessel in which he sailed for South Carolina, she would probably have lain wind-bound in Boston Harbor. It was ordained that the chair should not be taken away. Don't you think so, Grandfather?"

"It was kept here for Grandfather and me to sit in together," said little Alice, "and for Grandfather to tell stories about."

"And Grandfather is very glad of such a companion, and such a theme," said the old gentleman, with a smile. "Well, Laurence, if our oaken chair, like the wooden Palladium† of Troy, was connected with the country's fate, yet there appears to have been no supernatural obstacle to its removal from the Province House. In 1760, Sir Francis Bernard, who had been governor of New Jersey, was appointed to the same office in Massachusetts. He looked at the old chair, and thought it quite too shabby to keep company with a new set of mahogany chairs, and an aristocratic sofa, which had just arrived from London. He therefore ordered it to be put away in the garret."

The children were loud in their exclamations against this irreverent conduct of Sir Francis Bernard. But Grandfather defended him, as well as he could. He observed that it was then thirty years since the chair had been beautified by Governor Belcher. Most of the gilding was worn off by the frequent scourings which it had undergone, beneath the hands of a black slave. The damask cushion, once so splendid, was now squeezed out of all shape, and absolutely in tatters, so many were the ponderous† gentlemen who had deposited their weight upon it, during these thirty years.

LT. GOVERNOR HUTCHINSON

Moreover, at a council held by the Earl of Loudon with the governors of New England, in 1757, his lordship, in a moment of passion, had kicked over the chair with his military boot. By this unprovoked and unjustifiable act, our venerable friend had suffered a fracture of one of its rungs.

"But," said Grandfather, "our chair, after all, was not destined to spend the remainder of its days in the inglorious obscurity of a garret. Thomas Hutchinson, lieutenant-governor of the province, was told of Sir Francis Bernard's design. This gentleman was more familiar with the history of New England than any other man alive. He knew all the adventures and vicissitudes through which the old chair had passed, and could have told, as accurately as your own Grandfather, who were the personages that had occupied it. Often, while visiting at the Province House, he had eyed the chair with admiration, and felt a longing desire to become the possessor of it. He now waited upon Sir Francis Bernard, and easily obtained leave to carry it home."

"And I hope," said Clara, "he had it varnished and gilded anew."

"No," answered Grandfather. "What Mr. Hutchinson desired was to restore the chair, as much as possible, to its original aspect, such as it had appeared, when it was first made out of the Earl of Lincoln's oak tree. For this purpose he ordered it to be well scoured with soap and sand and polished with wax, and then provided it with a substantial leather cushion. When all was completed to his mind, he sat down in the old chair, and began to write his *History of Massachusetts.*"

"Oh, that was a bright thought in Mr. Hutchinson!" exclaimed Laurence. "And, no doubt, the dim figures of the former possessors of the chair flitted around him, as he wrote, and inspired him with a knowledge of all that they had done and suffered while on earth."

"Why, my dear Laurence," replied Grandfather, smiling, "if Mr. Hutchinson was favored with any such extraordinary inspiration, he made but a poor use of it in his *History*; for a duller piece of composition never came from any man's pen. However, he was accurate, at least, though far from possessing the brilliancy or philosophy of Mr. Bancroft."‡

"But, if Hutchinson knew the history of the chair," rejoined Laurence, "his heart must have been stirred by it."

"It must, indeed," said Grandfather. "It would be entertaining and instructive, at the present day, to imagine what were Mr. Hutchinson's thoughts, as he looked back upon the long vista of events with which this chair was so remarkably connected."

And Grandfather allowed his fancy to shape out an image of Lieutenant-Governor Hutchinson, sitting in an evening reverie by his fireside, and meditating on the changes that had slowly passed around the chair.

A devoted monarchist,† Hutchinson would heave no sigh for the subversion of the original republican† government, the purest that the world had seen, with which the colony began its existence. While reverencing the grim and stern old Puritans as the founders of his native land, he would not wish to recall them from their graves, nor to awaken again that king-resisting spirit, which he imagined to be laid asleep with them forever. Winthrop, Dudley, Bellingham, Endicott, Leverett, and Bradstreet! All these had had their day. Ages might come and go, but never again would the people's suffrages† place a republican governor in their ancient Chair of State!

Coming down to the epoch of the second charter, Hutchinson thought of the ship carpenter Phips, springing from the lowest of the people, and attaining to the loftiest station in the land. But, he smiled to perceive that this governor's example would awaken no turbulent ambition in the lower orders, for it was a king's gracious boon† alone that made the ship carpenter a ruler. Hutchinson rejoiced to mark the gradual growth of an aristocratic class, to whom the common people, as in duty bound, were learning humbly to resign the honors, emoluments,† and authority of state. He saw,–or else deceived himself–that throughout this epoch, the people's disposition to self-government had been growing weaker, through long disuse, and now existed only as a faint traditionary feeling.

The Lieutenant-Governor's reverie† had now come down to the period at which he himself was sitting in the historic chair. He endeavored to throw his glance forward, over the coming years. There, probably, he saw visions of hereditary rank, for himself and other aristocratic colonists. He saw the fertile fields of New England, portioned out among a few great landholders, and descending by entail† from generation to generation. He saw the people a race of tenantry, dependent on their lords. He saw stars, garters, coronets, and castles.

"But," added Grandfather, turning to Laurence, "the Lieutenant-Governor's castles were built nowhere but among the red embers of the fire, before which he was sitting. And, just as he had constructed a baronial residence for himself and his posterity, the fire rolled down upon the hearth, and crumbled it to ashes!"

Grandfather now looked at his watch, which hung within a beautiful little ebony Temple, supported by four Ionic† columns. He then laid his hand on the golden locks of little Alice, whose head had sunk down upon the arm of our illustrious chair.

"To bed, to bed, dear child!" said he. "Grandfather has put you to sleep, already, by his stories about these Famous Old People!"

Appendix II: Account of the Deportation of the Acadians

From Haliburton's *Historical and Statistical Account of Nova Scotia*

At a consultation, held between Colonel Winslow and Captain Murray, [of the New England forces, charged with the duty of exiling the Acadians,] it was agreed that a proclamation should be issued at the different settlements, requiring the attendance of the people at the respective posts on the same day; which proclamation should be so ambiguous† in its nature that the object for which they were to assemble could not be discerned, and so peremptory† in its terms as to ensure implicit† obedience. This instrument, having been drafted and approved, was distributed according to the original plan. That which was addressed to the people inhabiting the country now comprised within the limits of King's County, was as follows: –

"To the inhabitants of the District of Grand Pré, Minas, River Canard, &c.; as well ancient, as young men and lads:

"Whereas, his Excellency the Governor has instructed us of his late resolution, respecting the matter proposed to the inhabitants, and has ordered us to communicate the same in person, his Excellency being desirous that each of them should be fully satisfied of his Majesty's intentions, which he has also ordered us to communicate to you, such as they have been given to him. We, therefore, order and strictly enjoin, by these presents, all of the inhabitants, as well of the above named district as of all the other Districts, both old men and young men, as well as all the lads of ten years of age, to attend at the Church at Grand Pré, on Friday, the fifth instant, at three of the clock in the afternoon, that we may impart to them what we are ordered to communicate to them; declaring that no excuse will be admitted on any pretence whatever, on pain of forfeiting goods and chattels, in default of real estate. Given at Grand Pré, 2d September, 1755, and 29th year of his Majesty's Reign.

"JOHN WINSLOW."

In obedience to this summons four hundred and eighteen able-bodied men assembled. These being shut into the church (for that, too, had become an arsenal), Colonel Winslow placed himself, with his officers, in the center, and addressed them thus:–

"GENTLEMEN:

"I have received from his Excellency Governor Lawrence, the King's Commission, which I have in my hand; and by his orders you are convened together to manifest to you, his Majesty's final resolution to the French inhabitants of this his Province of Nova Scotia; who, for almost half a century, have had more indulgence granted them than any of his subjects in any part of his dominions; what use you have made of it you yourselves best know. The part of duty I am now upon, though necessary, is very disagreeable to my natural make and temper, as I know it must be grievous to you, who are of the same species; but it is not my business to animadvert† but to obey such orders as I receive, and therefore, without hesitation, shall deliver you his Majesty's orders and instructions, namely–that your lands and tenements, cattle of all kinds and live stock of all sorts, are forfeited† to the Crown; with all other your effects, saving your money and household goods, and you yourselves to be removed from this his Province.

"Thus it is peremptorily† his Majesty's orders that the whole French inhabitants of these Districts be removed; and I am, through his Majesty's goodness, directed to allow you liberty to carry of your money and household goods, as many as you can without discommoding† the vessels you go in. I shall do everything in my power that all those goods be secured to you, and that you are not molested† in carrying them off; also, that whole families shall go in the same vessel, and make this remove, which I am sensible must give you a great deal of trouble, as easy as his Majesty's service will admit; and hope that, in whatever part of the world you may fall, you may be faithful subjects, a peaceable and happy people. I must also inform you, that it is his Majesty's pleasure that you remain in security under the inspection and direction of the troops that I have the honor to command."

And he then declared them the King's prisoners. The whole number of persons collected at Grand Pré finally amounted to four hundred and eighty-three men, and three hundred and thirty-seven women, heads of families; and their sons and daughters, to five hundred and twenty-seven of the former, and five hundred and seventy-six of the latter; making in the whole one thousand nine hundred and twenty-three souls. Their stock consisted of one thousand two hundred and sixty-nine oxen, one thousand five hundred and fifty-seven cows, five thousand and seven young cattle, four hundred and ninety-three horses, eight thousand six hundred and ninety sheep, and four thousand one hundred and ninety-seven hogs. As some of these wretched inhabitants escaped to the woods, all possible measures were adopted to force them back to captivity. The country was laid waste to prevent

ACADIAN EXILES

their subsistence. In the District of Minas alone, there were destroyed two hundred and fifty-five houses, two hundred and seventy-six barns, one hundred and fifty-five outhouses, eleven mills, and one church; and the friends of those who refused to surrender were threatened as the victims of their obstinacy†.

In short, so operative were the terrors that surrounded them, that of twenty-four young men, who deserted from a transport, twenty-two were glad to return of themselves, the others being shot by sentinels; and one of their friends, who was supposed to have been accessory to their escape, was carried on shore to behold the destruction of his house and effects, which were burned in his presence, as a punishment for his temerity† and perfidious† aid to his comrades. The prisoners expressed the greatest concern at having incurred his Majesty's displeasure, and in a petition addressed to Colonel Winslow entreated him to detain a part of them as sureties† for the appearance of the rest, who were desirous of visiting their families, and consoling them in their distress and misfortunes. To comply with this request of holding a few as hostages for the surrender of the whole body, was deemed inconsistent with his instructions; but, as there could be no objection to allow a small number of them to return to their homes, permission was given to them to choose ten for the District of Minas (Horton) and ten for the District of Canard (Cornwallis) to whom leave of absence was given for one day, and on whose return a similar number were indulged in the same manner. They bore their confinement, and received their sentence with a fortitude and resignation altogether unexpected; but when the hour of embarkation† arrived, in which they were to leave the land of their nativity forever–to part with their friends and relatives, without the hope of ever seeing them again, and to be dispersed among strangers, whose language, customs and religion were opposed to their own, the weakness of human nature prevailed, and they were overpowered with the sense of their miseries. The preparations having been all completed, the 10th of September was fixed upon as the day of departure. The prisoners were drawn up six deep, and the young men, one hundred and sixty-one in number, were ordered to go first on board of the vessels. This they instantly and peremptorily refused to do, declaring that they would not leave their parents; but expressed a willingness to comply with the order, provided they were permitted to embark with their families. This request was immediately rejected, and the troops were ordered to fix bayonets and advance towards the prisoners, a motion which had the effect of producing obedience on the part of the young men, who forthwith commenced their march. The road from the chapel to the shore, just one mile in length, was crowded with women and children; who, on their knees, greeted them as they passed with their tears and their blessings, while the prisoners advanced with slow and reluctant steps, weeping, praying, and singing hymns. This detachment was followed by the seniors, who passed through the same scene of sorrow and distress. In this manner was the whole male part of the population of the District of Minas put on board the five transports, stationed in the river Gaspereaux, each vessel being guarded by six non-commissioned officers, and eighty privates. As soon as the other vessels arrived, their wives and children followed, and the whole were transported from Nova Scotia. The haste with which these measures were carried into execution did not admit of those preparations for their comfort, which, if unmerited by their disloyalty, were at least due in pity to the severity of their punishment. The hurry, confusion, and excitement connected with the embarkation had scarcely subsided, when the Provincials were appalled by the work of their own hands. The novelty and peculiarity of their situation could not but force itself upon the attention of even the unreflecting soldiery; stationed in the midst of a beautiful and fertile country, they suddenly found themselves without a foe to subdue, and without a population to protect. The volumes of smoke which the half-expiring embers emitted, while they marked the site of the peasant's humble cottage, bore testimony to the extent of the work of destruction. For several successive events the cattle assembled round the smoldering ruins, as if in anxious expectation of the return of their masters, while all night long the faithful watchdogs of the Neutrals howled over the scene of desolation, and mourned alike the hand that had fed, and the house that had sheltered them.

Part Three

1763-1803
Liberty Tree
The Last Words of Grandfather's Chair

Chapter I
A New Year's Day

On the evening of New Year's day, Grandfather was walking to and fro, across the carpet, listening to the rain which beat hard against the curtained windows. The riotous blast shook the casement, as if a strong man were striving to force his entrance into the comfortable room. With every puff of the wind, the fire leaped upward from the hearth, laughing and rejoicing at the shrieks of the wintry storm.

Meanwhile, Grandfather's chair stood in its customary place by the fireside. The bright blaze gleamed upon the fantastic figures of its oaken back, and shone through the open-work, so that a complete pattern was thrown upon the opposite side of the room. Sometimes, for a moment or two, the shadow remained immovable, as if it were painted on the wall. Then, all at once, it began to quiver, and leap, and dance, with a frisky motion. Anon,† seeming to remember that these antics were unworthy of such a dignified and venerable chair, it suddenly stood still. But soon it began to dance anew.

"Only see how grandfather's chair is dancing!" cried little Alice.

And she ran to the wall, and tried to catch hold of the flickering shadow; for to children of five years old, a shadow seems almost as real as a substance.

"I wish," said Clara, "Grandfather would sit down in the chair, and finish its history."

If the children had been looking at Grandfather, they would have noticed that he paused in his walk across the room, when Clara made this remark. The kind old gentleman was ready and willing to resume his stories of departed times. But he had resolved to wait till his auditors should request him to proceed, in order that they might find the instructive history of the chair a pleasure, and not a task.

"Grandfather," said Charley, "I am tired to death of this dismal rain, and of hearing the wind roar in the chimney. I have had no good time all day. It would be better to hear stories about the chair, than to sit doing nothing, and thinking of nothing."

To say the truth, our friend Charley was very much out of humor with the storm, because it had kept him all day within doors, and hindered him from making trial of a splendid sled, which Grandfather had given him for a New Year's gift. As all sleds, now-a-days, must have a name, the one in question had been honored with the title of *Grandfather's Chair*, which was painted in golden letters, on each of the sides. Charley greatly admired the construction of the new vehicle, and felt certain that it would outstrip any other sled that ever dashed down the long slopes of the Common.

As for Laurence, he happened to be thinking, just at this moment, about the history of the chair. Kind old Grandfather had made him a present of a volume of engraved portraits, representing the features of eminent and famous people of all countries. Among them Laurence found several who had formerly occupied our chair, or been connected with its adventures. While Grandfather walked to and fro across the room, the imaginative boy was gazing at the historic chair. He endeavored to summon up the portraits which he had seen in his volume, and to place them, like living figures, in the empty seat.

"The old chair has begun another year of its existence, today," said Laurence. "We must make haste, or it will have a new history to be told before we finish the old one."

"Yes, my children," replied Grandfather, with a smile and a sigh, "another year has been added to those of the two centuries, and upward, which have passed since the Lady Arbella brought this chair over from England. It is three times as old as your Grandfather; but a year makes no impression on its oaken frame, while it bends the old man nearer and nearer to the earth; so let me go on with my stories while I may."

Accordingly, Grandfather came to the fireside, and seated himself in the venerable chair. The lion's head looked down with a grimly good-natured aspect, as the children clustered around the old gentleman's knees. It almost seemed as if a real lion were peeping over the back of the chair, and smiling at the group of auditors, with a sort of lion-like complaisance. Little Alice, whose fancy often inspired her with singular ideas, exclaimed that the lion's head was nodding at her, and that it looked as if it were going to open its wide jaws and tell a story.

But, as the lion's head appeared to be in no haste to speak, and as there was no record or tradition of its having spoken, during the whole existence of the chair, Grandfather did not consider it worthwhile to wait.

Chapter II
The Stamp Act

"Charley, my boy," said Grandfather, "do you remember who was the last occupant of the chair?"

"It was Lieutenant-Governor Hutchinson," answered Charley. "Sir Francis Bernard, the new governor, had given him the chair, instead of putting it away in the garret of the Province House. And when we took leave of Hutchinson, he was sitting by his fireside, and thinking of the past adventures of the chair, and of what was to come."

"Very well," said Grandfather; "and you recollect that this was in 1763, or thereabouts, at the close of the Old French War. Now, that you may fully comprehend the remaining adventures of the chair, I must make some brief remarks on the situation and character of the New England colonies at this period."

So Grandfather spoke of the earnest loyalty of our fathers during the Old French War, and after the conquest of Canada had brought that war to a triumphant close.

The people loved and reverenced the king of England, even more than if the ocean had not rolled its waves between him and them; for, at the distance of three thousand miles, they could not discover his bad qualities and imperfections. Their love was increased by the dangers which they had encountered in order to heighten his glory and extend his dominion. Throughout the war, the American colonists had fought side by side with the soldiers of Old England; and nearly thirty thousand young men had laid down their lives for the honor of King George. And the survivors loved him the better, because they had done and suffered so much for his sake.

KING GEORGE III‡

But, there were some circumstances that caused America to feel more independent of England than at an earlier period. Canada and Acadia had now become British provinces; and our fathers were no longer afraid of the bands of French and Indians, who used to assault them in old times. For a century and a half this had been the great terror of New England. Now, the old French soldier was driven from the north forever. And, even had it been otherwise, the English colonies were growing so populous and powerful that they might have felt fully able to protect themselves without any help from England.

There were thoughtful and sagacious† men, who began to doubt, whether a great country like America, would always be content to remain under the government of an island three thousand miles away. This was the more doubtful, because the English Parliament had long ago made laws which were intended to be very beneficial to England, at the expense of America. By these laws, the colonists were forbidden to manufacture articles for their own use, or to carry on trade with any nation but the English.

"Now," continued Grandfather, "if King George the Third and his councilors had considered these things wisely, they would have taken another course than they did. But, when they saw how rich and populous the colonies had grown, their first thought was, how they might make more profit out of them than heretofore. England was enormously in debt, at the close of the Old French War, and it was pretended that this debt had been contracted for the defense of the American colonies, and that therefore a part of it ought to be paid by them."

"Why, this was nonsense," exclaimed Charley; "did not our fathers spend their lives and their money too, to get

PATRIOTS READING THE STAMP ACT

Canada for King George?"

"True, they did," said Grandfather; "and they told the English rulers so. But the king and his ministers would not listen to good advice. In 1765, the British Parliament passed a Stamp Act."

"What was that?" inquired Charley.

"The Stamp Act," replied Grandfather, "was a law by which all deeds, bonds, and other papers of the same kind, were ordered to be marked with the king's stamp; and without this mark, they were declared illegal and void. Now, in order to get a blank sheet of paper, with the king's stamp upon it, people were obliged to pay three pence more than the actual value of the paper. And this extra sum of three pence was a tax, and was to be paid into the king's treasury."

"I am sure three pence was not worth quarrelling about!" remarked Clara.

"It was not for three pence, nor for any amount of money, that America quarreled with England," replied Grandfather; "it was for a great principle. The colonists were determined not to be taxed, except by their own representatives. They said that neither the king and Parliament nor any other power on earth, had a right to take their money out of their pockets, unless they freely gave it. And, rather than pay three pence when it was unjustly demanded, they resolved to sacrifice all the wealth of the country, and their lives along with it. They therefore made a most stubborn resistance to the Stamp Act."‡

"That was noble!" exclaimed Laurence. "I understand how it was. If they had quietly paid this tax of three pence, they would have ceased to be freemen, and would have become tributaries† of England. And so they contended about a great question of right and wrong, and put every thing at stake for it."

"You are right, Laurence," said Grandfather; "and it was really amazing and terrible to see what a change came over the aspect of the people, the moment the English Parliament had passed this oppressive act. The former history of our chair, my children, has given you some idea of what a harsh, unyielding, stern set of men the old Puritans were. For a good many years back, however, it had seemed as if these characteristics were disappearing. But no sooner did England offer wrong to the colonies, than the descendants of the early settlers proved that they had the same kind of temper as their forefathers. The moment before, New England appeared like an humble and loyal subject of the crown; the next instant, she showed the grim, dark features of an old king-resisting Puritan."

Grandfather spoke briefly of the public measures that were taken in opposition to the Stamp Act. As this law affected all the American colonies alike, it naturally led them to think of consulting together in order to procure its repeal. For this purpose, the legislature of Massachusetts proposed that delegates† from every colony should meet in Congress. Accordingly nine colonies, both northern and southern, sent delegates to the city of New York.

"And did they consult about going to war with England?" asked Charley.

"No, Charley," answered Grandfather; "a great deal of talking was yet to be done, before England and America could come to blows. The Congress stated the rights and the grievances of the colonists. They sent an humble petition to the king, and a memorial to the Parliament, beseeching that the Stamp Act might be repealed. This was all that the delegates had it in their power to do."

"They might as well have stayed at home, then," said Charley.

"By no means," replied Grandfather. "It was a most important and memorable event–this first coming together of the American people, by their representatives from the north and south. If England had been wise, she would have trembled at the first word that was spoken in such an assembly!"

These remonstrances† and petitions,† as Grandfather observed, were the work of grave, thoughtful, and prudent† men. Meantime, the young and hot-headed people went to work in their own way. It is probable that the petitions of Congress would have had little or no effect on the British statesmen, if the violent deeds of the American people had not shown how much excited the people were. Liberty Tree was soon heard of in England.

"What was Liberty Tree?" inquired Clara.

"It was an old elm tree," answered Grandfather, "which stood near the corner of Essex Street, opposite the Boylston market. Under the spreading branches of this great tree, the people used to assemble, whenever they wished to express their feelings and opinions. Thus, after a while, it seemed as if the liberty of the country was connected with Liberty Tree."

"It was glorious fruit for a tree to bear," remarked Laurence.

"It bore strange fruit, sometimes," said Grandfather. "One morning in August, 1765, two figures were found hanging on the sturdy branches of Liberty Tree.‡ They were dressed in square-skirted coats and breeches; and, as their wigs hung down over their faces, they looked like real men. One was intended to represent the Earl of Bute, who was supposed to have advised the king to tax America. The other was meant for the effigy of Andrew Oliver, a gentleman belonging to one of the most respectable families in Massachusetts."

"What harm had he done?" inquired Charley.

"The king had appointed him to be distributor of the stamps," answered Grandfather. "Mr. Oliver would have made a great deal of money by this business. But the people frightened him so much by hanging him in effigy,† and afterwards by breaking into his house, that he promised to have nothing to do with the stamps. And all the king's friends throughout America were compelled to make the same promise."

Chapter III
The Hutchinson Mob

"Lieutenant-Governor Hutchinson," continued Grandfather, "now began to be unquiet in our old chair. He had formerly been much respected and beloved by the people, and had often proved himself a friend to their interests. But the time was come, when he could not be a friend to the people, without ceasing to be a friend to the king. It was pretty generally understood that Hutchinson would act according to the king's wishes, right or wrong, like most of the other gentlemen who held offices under the crown. Besides, as he was brother-in-law of Andrew Oliver, the people now felt a particular dislike to him."

"I should think," said Laurence, "as Mr. Hutchinson had written the history of our Puritan forefathers, he would have known what the temper of the people was, and so have taken care not to wrong them."

"He trusted in the might of the king of England," replied Grandfather, "and thought himself safe under the shelter of the throne. If no dispute had arisen between the king and the people, Hutchinson would have had the character of a wise, good, and patriotic magistrate. But, from the time that he took part against the rights of his country, the people's love and respect were turned to scorn and hatred; and he never had another hour of peace."

In order to show what a fierce and dangerous spirit was now aroused among the inhabitants, Grandfather related a passage from history, which we shall call

The Hutchinson Mob

On the evening of the twenty-sixth of August, 1765, a bonfire was kindled in King Street. It flamed high upward, and threw a ruddy light over the front of the Town House, on which was displayed a carved representation of the royal arms. The gilded vane of the cupola glittered in the blaze. The kindling of this bonfire was the well-known signal for the populace of Boston to assemble in the street.

Before the tar barrels, of which the bonfire was made, were half burnt out, a great crowd had come together. They were chiefly laborers and seafaring men, together with many young apprentices, and all those idle people about town who are ready for any kind of mischief. Doubtless some schoolboys were among them.

While these rough figures stood round the blazing bonfire, you might hear them speaking bitter words against the high officers of the province. Governor Bernard, Hutchinson, Oliver, Storey, Hallowell, and other men whom King George delighted to honor, were reviled as traitors to the country. Now and then, perhaps, an officer of the crown passed along the street, wearing the gold-laced hat, white wig, and embroidered waistcoat, which were the fashion of the day. But, when the people beheld him, they set up a wild and angry howl, and their faces had an evil aspect, which was made more terrible by the flickering blaze of the bonfire.

"I should like to throw the traitor right into that blaze!" perhaps one fierce rioter would say.

"Yes; and all his brethren too!" another might reply; "and the governor and old Tommy Hutchinson into the hottest of it!"

"And the Earl of Bute along with them," muttered a third; "and burn the whole pack of them under King George's nose! No matter if it singed him!"

Some such expressions as these, either shouted aloud, or muttered under the breath, were doubtless heard in King Street. The mob, meanwhile, were growing fiercer, and fiercer, and seemed ready even to set the town on fire, for the sake of burning the king's friends out of house and home. And yet, angry as they were, they sometimes broke into a loud roar of laughter, as if mischief and destruction were their sport.

But we must now leave the rioters for a time, and take a peep into the lieutenant-governor's splendid mansion. It was a large brick house, decorated with Ionic pilasters,† and stood in Garden Court Street, near the North Square.

While the angry mob in King Street were shouting his name, Lieutenant-Governor Hutchinson sat quietly in Grandfather's chair, unsuspicious of the evil that was about to fall upon his head. His beloved family were in the room with him. He had thrown off his embroidered coat and powdered wig, and had on a loose-flowing gown and purple velvet cap. He had likewise laid aside the cares of state, and all the thoughts that had wearied and perplexed him

A NEIGHBOR WARNS LT. GOVERNOR HUTCHINSON

throughout the day.

Perhaps, in the enjoyment of his home, he had forgotten all about the Stamp Act, and scarcely remembered that there was a king, across the ocean, who had resolved to make tributaries of the New Englanders. Possibly, too, he had forgotten his own ambition, and would not have exchanged his situation, at that moment, to be governor, or even a lord.

The wax candles were now lighted, and showed a handsome room, well provided with rich furniture. On the walls hung the pictures of Hutchinson's ancestors, who had been eminent men in their day, and were honorably remembered in the history of the country. Every object served to mark the residence of a rich, aristocratic gentleman, who held himself high above the common people, and could have nothing to fear from them. In a corner of the room, thrown carelessly upon a chair, were the scarlet robes of the chief justice. This high office, as well as those of lieutenant-governor, councillor, and judge of probate, was filled by Hutchinson.

Who or what could disturb the domestic quiet of such a great and powerful personage as now sat in Grandfather's chair?

The lieutenant-governor's favorite daughter sat by his side. She leaned on the arm of our great chair, and looked up affectionately into her father's face, rejoicing to perceive that a quiet smile was on his lips. But suddenly a shade came across her countenance. She seemed to listen attentively, as if to catch a distant sound.

"What is the matter, my child?" inquired Hutchinson.

"Father, do not you hear a tumult[†] in the streets?" said she.

The lieutenant-governor listened. But his ears were duller than those of his daughter; he could hear nothing more terrible than the sound of a summer breeze, sighing among the tops of the elm trees.

"No, foolish child!" he replied, playfully patting her cheek. "There is no tumult. Our Boston mobs are satisfied with what mischief they have already done. The king's friends need not tremble."

So Hutchinson resumed his pleasant and peaceful meditations, and again forgot that there were any troubles in the world. But his family were alarmed, and could not help straining their ears to catch the slightest sound. More and more distinctly they heard shouts, and then the trampling of many feet. While they were listening, one of the neighbors rushed breathless into the room.

"A mob! A terrible mob!" cried he: "They have broken into Mr. Storey's house, and into Mr. Hallowell's, and have made themselves drunk with the liquors in his cellar, and now they are coming hither, as wild as so many tigers. Flee, Lieutenant-Governor, for your life! For your life!"

"Father, dear Father, make haste!" shrieked his children.

But Hutchinson would not hearken to them. He was an old lawyer; and he could not realize that the people would do any thing so utterly lawless as to assault him in his peaceful home. He was one of King George's chief officers; and it would be an insult and outrage upon the king himself, if the lieutenant-governor should suffer any wrong.

"Have no fears on my account," said he; "I am perfectly safe. The king's name shall be my protection."

Yet he bade his family retire into one of the neighboring houses. His daughter would have remained, but he forced her away.

THE HUTCHINSON MOB

The huzzas and riotous uproar of the mob were now heard, close at hand. The sound was terrible, and struck Hutchinson with the same sort of dread as if an enraged wild beast had broken loose, and were roaring for its prey. He crept softly to the window. There he beheld an immense concourse† of people, filling all the street, and rolling onward to his house. It was like a tempestuous flood that had swelled beyond its bounds, and would sweep every thing before it. Hutchinson trembled; he felt, at that moment, that the wrath of the people was a thousandfold more terrible than the wrath of a king.

That was a moment when a loyalist and an aristocrat, like Hutchinson, might have learned how powerless are kings, nobles, and great men, when the low and humble range themselves against them. King George could do nothing for his servant now. Had King George been there, he could have done nothing for himself. If Hutchinson had understood this lesson, and remembered it, he need not, in after years, have been an exile from his native country, nor finally have laid his bones in a distant land.

There was now a rush against the doors of the house. The people sent up a hoarse cry. At this instant, the lieutenant-governor's daughter, whom he had supposed to be in a place of safety, ran into the room, and threw her arms around him. She had returned by a private entrance.

"Father, are you mad!" cried she. "Will the king's name protect you now? Come with me, or they will have your life."

"True," muttered Hutchinson to himself; "what care these roarers for the name of king? I must flee, or they will trample me down, on the door of my own dwelling!"

Hurrying away, he and his daughter made their escape by the private passage, at the moment when the rioters broke into the house. The foremost of them rushed up the staircase, and entered the room which Hutchinson had just quitted. There they beheld our good old chair, facing them with quiet dignity, while the lion's head seemed to move its jaws in the unsteady light of their torches. Perhaps the stately aspect of our venerable friend, which had stood firm through a century and a half of trouble, arrested them for an instant. But they were thrust forward by those behind, and the chair lay overthrown.

Then began the work of destruction. The carved and polished mahogany tables were shattered with heavy clubs, and hewn to splinters with axes. The marble hearths and mantel pieces were broken. The volumes of Hutchinson's library, so precious to a studious man, were torn out of their covers, and the leaves sent flying out of the windows. Manuscripts, containing secrets of our country's history, which are now lost forever, were scattered to the winds.

The old ancestral portraits, whose fixed countenances looked down on the wild scene, were rent from the walls.

FLIGHT OF HUTCHINSON BEFORE THE MOB

The mob triumphed in their downfall and destruction, as if these pictures of Hutchinson's forefathers had committed the same offences as their descendant. A tall looking-glass, which had hitherto presented a reflection of the enraged and drunken multitude, was now smashed into a thousand fragments. We gladly dismiss the scene from the mirror of our fancy.

Before morning dawned, the walls of the house were all that remained. The interior was a dismal scene of ruin. A shower pattered in at the broken windows, and when Hutchinson and his family returned, they stood shivering in the same room, where the last evening had seen them so peaceful and happy.

***

"Grandfather," said Laurence indignantly, "if the people acted in this manner, they were not worthy of even so much liberty as the king of England was willing to allow them."

"It was a most unjustifiable act, like many other popular movements at that time," replied Grandfather. "But we must not decide against the justice of the people's cause, merely because an excited mob was guilty of outrageous violence. Besides, all these things were done in the first fury of resentment. Afterwards, the people grew more calm, and were more influenced by the counsel of those wise and good men who conducted them safely and gloriously through the Revolution."

Little Alice, with tears in her blue eyes, said that she hoped the neighbors had not let Lieutenant-Governor Hutchinson and his family be homeless in the street, but had taken them into their houses, and been kind to them. Cousin Clara, recollecting the perilous situation of our beloved chair, inquired what had become of it.

"Nothing was heard of our chair for sometime afterwards," answered Grandfather. "One day in September, the same Andrew Oliver, of whom I before told you, was summoned to appear at high noon, under Liberty Tree. This was the strangest summons that had ever been heard of; for it was issued in the name of the whole people, who thus took upon themselves the authority of a sovereign power. Mr. Oliver dared not disobey. Accordingly, at the appointed hour, he went, much against his will, to Liberty Tree."

Here Charley interposed a remark that poor Mr. Oliver found but little liberty under Liberty Tree. Grandfather assented.

"It was a stormy day," continued he. "The equinoctial† gale blew violently, and scattered the yellow leaves of Liberty Tree all along the street. Mr. Oliver's wig was dripping with water drops, and he probably looked haggard, disconsolate, and humbled to the earth. Beneath the tree, in Grandfather's chair,–our own venerable chair,–sat Mr. Richard Dana, a justice of the peace. He administered an oath to Mr. Oliver, that he would never have anything to do with distributing the stamps. A vast concourse of people heard the oath, and shouted when it was taken."

"There is something grand in this," said Laurence. "I like it, because the people seem to have acted with thoughtfulness and dignity; and this proud gentleman, one of his Majesty's high officers, was made to feel that King George could not protect him in doing wrong."

"But it was a sad day for poor Mr. Oliver,"‡ observed Grandfather. "From his youth upward, it had probably been the great principle of his life, to be faithful and obedient to the king. And now, in his old age, it must have puzzled and distracted him, to find the sovereign people setting up a claim to his faith and obedience."

Grandfather closed the evening's conversation by saying that the discontent of America was so great, that in 1766, the British Parliament was compelled to repeal the Stamp Act. The people made great rejoicings, but took care to keep Liberty Tree well pruned, and free from caterpillars and canker worms. They foresaw that there might yet be occasion for them to assemble under its far-projecting shadow.

Chapter IV
The British Troops in Boston

The next evening, Clara, who remembered that our chair had been left standing in the rain, under Liberty Tree, earnestly besought Grandfather to tell when and where it had next found shelter. Perhaps she was afraid that the venerable chair, by being exposed to the inclemency† of a September gale, might get the rheumatism in its aged joints.

"The chair," said Grandfather, "after the ceremony of Mr. Oliver's oath, appears to have been quite forgotten by the multitude. Indeed, being much bruised and rather rickety, owing to the violent treatment it had suffered from the Hutchinson mob, most people would have thought that its days of usefulness were over. Nevertheless, it was conveyed away, under cover of the night, and committed to the care of a skillful joiner. He doctored our old friend so successfully, that in the course of a few days, it made its appearance in the public room of the British Coffee House‡ in King Street."

"But why did not Mr. Hutchinson get possession of it again?" inquired Charley.

"I know not," answered Grandfather, "unless he considered it a dishonor and disgrace to the chair to have stood under Liberty Tree. At all events, he suffered it to remain at the British Coffee House, which was the principal hotel in

Boston. It could not possibly have found a situation, where it would be more in the midst of business and bustle, or would witness more important events, or be occupied by a greater variety of persons."

Grandfather went on to tell the proceedings of the despotic king and ministry of England, after the repeal of the Stamp Act. They could not bear to think that their right to tax America should be disputed by the people. In the year 1767, therefore, they caused Parliament to pass an act for laying a duty on tea, and some other articles that were in general use. Nobody could now buy a pound of tea, without paying a tax to King George. This scheme was pretty craftily contrived; for the women of America were very fond of tea, and did not like to give up the use of it.

But the people were as much opposed to this new act of Parliament, as they had been to the Stamp Act. England,

FANEUIL HALL

however, was determined that they should submit. In order to compel their obedience, two regiments, consisting of more than seven hundred British soldiers, were sent to Boston. They arrived in September, 1768, and were landed on Long Wharf. Thence they marched to the Common, with loaded muskets, fixed bayonets, and great pomp and parade. So now, at last, the free town of Boston was guarded and overawed by redcoats,† as it had been in the days of old Sir Edmund Andros.

In the month of November, more regiments arrived. There were now four thousand troops in Boston. The Common was whitened with their tents. Some of the soldiers were lodged in Faneuil Hall, which the inhabitants looked upon as a consecrated place, because it had been the scene of a great many meetings in favor of liberty. One regiment was placed in the Town House, which we now call the Old State House. The lower floor of this edifice had hitherto been used by the merchants as an exchange. In the upper stories were the chambers of the judges, the representatives, and the governor's council. The venerable councillors could not assemble to consult about the welfare of the province, without being challenged by sentinels,† and passing among the bayonets of the British soldiers.

Sentinels, likewise, were posted at the lodgings of the officers, in many parts of the town. When the inhabitants approached, they were greeted by the sharp question–"Who goes there?" while the rattle of the soldier's musket was heard, as he presented it against their breasts. There was no quiet, even on the Sabbath day. The pious descendants of the Puritans were shocked by the uproar of military music, the drum, fife, and bugle, drowning the holy organ peal and the voices of the singers. It would appear as if the British took every method to insult the feelings of the people.

"Grandfather," cried Charley, impatiently, "the people did not go to fighting half soon enough! These British redcoats ought to have been driven back to their vessels, the very moment they landed on Long Wharf."

"Many a hot-headed young man said the same as you do, Charley," answered Grandfather. "But the elder and wiser people saw that the time was not yet come. Meanwhile, let us take another peep at our old chair."

"Ah, it drooped its head, I know," said Charley, "when it saw how the province was disgraced. Its old Puritan friends never would have borne such doings."

"The chair," proceeded Grandfather, "was now continually occupied by some of the high Tories,† as the king's friends were called, who frequented the British Coffee House. Officers of the customhouse,† too, which stood on the opposite side of King Street, often sat in the chair, wagging their tongues against John Hancock."

"Why against him?" asked Charley.

"Because he was a great merchant, and contended against paying duties to the king," said Grandfather.

"Well, frequently, no doubt, the officers of the British regiments, when not on duty, used to fling themselves into the arms of our venerable chair. Fancy one of them, a red-nosed captain, in his scarlet uniform, playing with the hilt of his sword, and making a circle of his brother officers merry with ridiculous jokes at the expense of the poor Yankees.† And perhaps he would call for a bottle of wine, or a steaming

BRITISH SOLDIERS IN BOSTON

bowl of punch, and drink confusion to all rebels."

"Our grave old chair must have been scandalized at such scenes," observed Laurence. "The chair that had been the Lady Arbella's, and which the holy Apostle Eliot had consecrated."

"It certainly was little less than sacrilege," replied Grandfather; "but the time was coming, when even the churches, where hallowed pastors had long preached the word of God, were to be torn down or desecrated by the British troops. Some years passed, however, before such things were done."

Grandfather now told his auditors, that in 1769, Sir Francis Bernard went to England, after having been governor of

Massachusetts ten years. He was a gentleman of many good qualities, an excellent scholar, and a friend to learning. But he was naturally of an arbitrary disposition; and he had been bred at the University of Oxford, where young men were taught that the divine right of kings was the only thing to be regarded in matters of government. Such ideas were ill-adapted to please the people of Massachusetts. They rejoiced to get rid of Sir Francis Bernard, but liked his successor, Lieutenant-Governor Hutchinson, no better than himself.

About this period, the people were much incensed at an act, committed by a person who held an office in the customhouse. Some lads, or young men, were snowballing his windows. He fired a musket at them and killed a poor German boy,‡ only eleven years old. This event made a great noise in town and country, and much increased the resentment that was already felt against the servants of the crown.

"Now, children," said Grandfather, "I wish to make you comprehend the position of the British troops in King Street. This is the same which we now call State Street. On the south side of the Town House, or Old State House, was what military men call a court of guard, defended by two brass cannons, which pointed directly at one of the doors of the above edifice. A large party of soldiers were always stationed in the court of guard. The customhouse stood at a little distance down King Street, nearly where the Suffolk bank now stands; and a sentinel was continually pacing before its front."

"I shall remember this, tomorrow," said Charley; "and I will go to State Street, so as to see exactly where the British troops were stationed."

"And, before long," observed Grandfather, "I shall have to relate an event, which made King Street sadly famous on both sides of the Atlantic. The history of our chair will soon bring us to this melancholy business."

Here Grandfather described the state of things, which arose from the ill-will that existed between the inhabitants and the redcoats. The old and sober part of the townspeople were very angry at the government, for sending soldiers to overawe them. But those gray-headed men were cautious, and kept their thoughts and feelings in their own breasts, without putting themselves in the way of the British bayonets.

The younger people, however, could hardly be kept within such prudent limits. They reddened with wrath at the very sight of a soldier, and would have been willing to come to blows with them, at any moment. For it was their opinion that every tap of a British drum within the peninsula of Boston, was an insult to the brave old town.

"It was sometimes the case," continued Grandfather, "that affrays[†] happened between such wild young men as these, and small parties of the soldiers. No weapons had hitherto been used, except fists or cudgels. But, when men have loaded muskets in their hands, it is easy to foretell that they will soon be turned against the bosoms of those who provoke their anger."

"Grandfather," said little Alice, looking fearfully into his face, "your voice sounds as though you were going to tell us something awful!"

Chapter V
The Boston Massacre

Little Alice, by her last remark, proved herself a good judge of what was expressed by the tones of Grandfather's voice. He had given the above description of the enmity† between the townspeople and the soldiers, in order to prepare the minds of his auditors for a very terrible event. It was one that did more to heighten the quarrel between England and America, than any thing that had yet occurred.

Without further preface, Grandfather began the story of

The Boston Massacre

It was now the third of March, 1770. The sunset music of the British regiments was heard, as usual, throughout the town. The shrill fife and rattling drum awoke the echoes in King Street, while the last ray of sunshine was lingering on the cupola of the Town House. And now, all the sentinels were posted. One of them marched up and down before the customhouse, treading a short path through the snow, and longing for the time when he would be dismissed to the warm fireside of the guardroom. Meanwhile, Captain Preston was perhaps sitting in our great chair, before the hearth of the British Coffee House. In the course of the evening, there were two or three slight commotions, which seemed to indicate that trouble was at hand. Small parties of young men stood at the corners of the streets, or walked along the narrow pavements. Squads of soldiers, who were dismissed from duty, passed by them, shoulder to shoulder, with the regular step which they had learned at the drill. Whenever these encounters took place, it appeared to be the object of the young men to treat the soldiers with as much incivility as possible.

"Turn out, you lobster-backs!" one would say. "Crowd them off the sidewalks!" another would cry. "A redcoat has no right in Boston streets."

"Oh, you rebel rascals!" perhaps the soldiers would reply, glaring fiercely at the young men. "Some day or other, we'll make our way through Boston streets, at the point of the

FALL OF CRISPUS ATTUCKS,‡
FIRST CASUALTY OF THE AMERICAN REVOLUTION

BRISTISH SOLDIERS OPEN FIRE

bayonet!"

Once or twice, such disputes as these brought on a scuffle; which passed off, however, without attracting much notice. About eight o'clock, for some unknown cause, an alarm bell rang loudly and hurriedly.

At the sound, many people ran out of their houses, supposing it to be an alarm of fire. But there were no flames to be seen; nor was there any smell of smoke in the clear, frosty air; so that most of the townsmen went back to their own firesides, and sat talking with their wives and children about the calamities of the times. Others, who were younger and less prudent, remained in the streets; for there seems to have been a presentiment† that some strange event was on the eve of taking place.

Later in the evening, not far from nine o'clock, several young men passed by the Town House, and walked down King Street. The sentinel was still on his post, in front of the customhouse, pacing to and fro, while, as he turned, a gleam of light, from some neighboring window, glittered on the barrel of his musket. At no great distance were the barracks and the guardhouse, where his comrades were probably telling stories of battle and bloodshed.

Down towards the customhouse, as I told you, came a party of wild young men. When they drew near the sentinel, he halted on his post, and took his musket from his shoulder, ready to present the bayonet at their breasts.

"Who goes there?" he cried, in the gruff, peremptory tones of a soldier's challenge.

The young men, being Boston boys, felt as if they had a right to walk their own streets, without being accountable to a British redcoat, even though he challenged them in King George's name. They made some rude answer to the sentinel. There was a dispute, or, perhaps a scuffle. Other soldiers heard the noise, and ran hastily from the barracks, to assist their comrade. At the same time, many of the townspeople rushed into King Street, by various avenues, and gathered in a crowd round about the customhouse. It seemed wonderful how such a multitude had started up, all of a sudden.

The wrongs and insults, which the people had been suffering for many months, now kindled them into a rage. They threw snowballs and lumps of ice at the soldiers. As the tumult grew louder, it reached the ears of Captain Preston, the officer of the day. He immediately ordered eight soldiers of the main guard to take their muskets and follow him. They marched across the street, forcing their way roughly through the crowd, and pricking the townspeople with their bayonets.

A gentleman, (it was Henry Knox, afterwards general of the American artillery,) caught Captain Preston's arm.

"For Heaven's sake, Sir," exclaimed he, take heed what you do, or here will be bloodshed."

"Stand aside!" answered Captain Preston, haughtily. "Do not interfere, Sir. Leave me to manage the affair."

Arriving at the sentinel's post, Captain Preston drew up his men in a semi-circle, with their faces to the crowd and their rear to the customhouse. "When the people saw the officer, and beheld the threatening attitude with which the soldiers fronted them, their rage became almost uncontrollable.

"Fire, you lobster-backs!" bellowed some.

"You dare not fire, you cowardly redcoats," cried others.

"Rush upon them!" shouted many voices. "Drive the rascals to their barracks! Down with them! Down with

"FIRE, IF YOU DARE!"

them! Let them fire, if they dare!"

Amid the uproar, the soldiers stood glaring at the people, with the fierceness of men whose trade was to shed blood.

Oh, what a crisis had now arrived! Up to this very moment, the angry feelings between England and America might have been pacified. England had but to stretch out the hand of reconciliation, and acknowledge that she had hitherto mistaken her rights but would do so no more. Then, the ancient bonds of brotherhood would again have been knit together, as firmly as in old times. The habit of loyalty, which had grown as strong as instinct, was not utterly overcome. The perils shared, the victories won, in the Old French War, when the soldiers of the colonies fought side by side with their comrades from beyond the sea, were unforgotten yet. England was still that beloved country which the colonists called their home. King George, though he had frowned upon America, was still reverenced as a father.

But, should the king's soldiers shed one drop of American blood, then it was a quarrel to the death. Never–never would America rest satisfied, until she had torn down the royal authority, and trampled it in the dust.

"Fire, if you dare, villains!" hoarsely shouted the people, while the muzzles of the muskets were turned upon them; "You dare not fire!"

They appeared ready to rush upon the leveled bayonets. Captain Preston waved his sword, and uttered a command which could not be distinctly heard, amid the uproar of shouts that issued from a hundred throats. But his soldiers deemed that he had spoken the fatal mandate–"Fire!" The flash of their muskets lighted up the street, and the report rang loudly between the edifices. It was said, too, that the figure of a man with a cloth hanging down over his face, was seen to step into the balcony of the customhouse, and discharge a musket at the crowd.

A gush of smoke had overspread the scene. It rose heavily, as if it were loath to reveal the dreadful spectacle beneath it. Eleven of the sons of New England lay stretched upon the street. Some, sorely wounded, were struggling to rise again. Others stirred not, nor groaned, for they were past all pain. Blood was streaming upon the snow; and that purple stain, in the midst of King Street, though it melted away in the next day's sun, was never forgotten nor forgiven by the people.

***

Grandfather was interrupted by the violent sobs of little Alice. In his earnestness, he had neglected to soften down the narrative, so that it might not terrify the heart of this unworldly infant. Since Grandfather began the history of our chair, little Alice had listened to many tales of war. But, probably, the idea had never really impressed itself upon her mind, that men have shed the blood of their fellow creatures. And now that this idea was forcibly presented to her, it affected the sweet child with bewilderment and horror.

"I ought to have remembered our dear little Alice," said Grandfather reproachfully to himself. "Oh, what a pity! Her heavenly nature has now received its first impression of earthly sin and violence. Well, Clara, take her to bed, and comfort her. Heaven grant that she may dream away the recollection of the Boston Massacre!"

"Grandfather," said Charley, when Clara and little Alice

had retired, "did not the people rush upon the soldiers, and take revenge?"

"The town drums beat to arms," replied Grandfather, "the alarm bells rang, and an immense multitude rushed into King Street. Many of them had weapons in their hands. The British prepared to defend themselves. A whole regiment was drawn up in the street, expecting an attack; for the townsmen appeared ready to throw themselves upon the bayonets."

"And how did it end?" asked Charley.

"Governor Hutchinson hurried to the spot," said Grandfather, "and besought the people to have patience, promising that strict justice should be done. A day or two afterward, the British troops were withdrawn from town, and stationed at Castle William. Captain Preston and the eight soldiers were tried for murder. But none of them were found guilty. The judges told the jury that the insults and violence which had been offered to the soldiers, justified them in firing at the mob."

"The Revolution," observed Laurence, who had said but little during the evening, "was not such a calm, majestic movement as I supposed. I do not love to hear of mobs and broils in the street. These things were unworthy of the people, when they had such a great object to accomplish."

"Nevertheless, the world has seen no grander movement than that of our Revolution, from first to last," said Grandfather. "The people, to a man, were full of a great and noble sentiment. True, there may be much fault to find with their mode of expressing this sentiment; but they knew no better–the necessity was upon them to act out their feelings, in the best manner they could. We must forgive what was wrong in their actions, and look into their hearts and minds for the honorable motives that impelled them."

"And I suppose," said Laurence, "there were men who knew how to act worthily of what they felt."

"There were many such," replied Grandfather, "and we will speak of some of them, hereafter."

Grandfather here made a pause. That night, Charley had a dream about the Boston Massacre, and thought that he himself was in the crowd, and struck down Captain Preston with a great club. Laurence dreamed that he was sitting in our great chair, at the window of the British Coffee House, and beheld the whole scene which Grandfather had described. It seemed to him, in his dream, that if the townspeople and the soldiers would but have heard him speak a single word, all the slaughter might have been averted. But there was such an uproar that it drowned his voice.

The next morning, the two boys went together to State Street, and stood on the very spot where the first blood of the Revolution had been shed. The Old State House was still there, presenting almost the same aspect that it had worn on that memorable evening, one-and-seventy years ago. It is the sole remaining witness of the Boston Massacre.‡

Chapter VI
Not Ashamed of Her Sons

The next evening the astral† lamp was lighted earlier than usual, because Laurence was very much engaged in looking over the collection of portraits which had been his New Year's gift from Grandfather.

Among them he found the features of more than one famous personage who had been connected with the adventures of our old chair. Grandfather bade him draw the table nearer to the fireside; and they looked over the portraits together, while Clara and Charley likewise lent their attention. As for little Alice, she sat in Grandfather's lap, and seemed to see the very men alive, whose faces were there represented.

SAMUEL ADAMS

Turning over the volume, Laurence came to the portrait of a stern, grim-looking man, in plain attire, of much more modern fashion than that of the old Puritans. But the face might well have befitted one of those iron-hearted men. Beneath the portrait was the name of Samuel Adams.

"He was a man of great note in

JOHN HANCOCK

all the doings that brought about the Revolution," said Grandfather. "His character was such, that it seemed as if one of the ancient Puritans had been sent back to earth to animate the people's hearts with the same abhorrence of tyranny, that had distinguished the earliest settlers. He was as religious as they, as stern and inflexible, and as deeply imbued with democratic principles. He, better than any one else, may be taken as a representative of the people of New England, and of the spirit with which they engaged in the revolutionary struggle. He was a poor man, and earned his bread by an humble occupation; but with his tongue and pen, he made the King of England tremble on his throne. Remember him, my children, as one of the strong men of our country."

JOSEPH WARREN

"Here is one whose looks show a very different character," observed Laurence, turning to the portrait of John Hancock. "I should think, by his splendid dress and courtly aspect, that he was one of the king's friends."

"There never was a greater contrast than between Samuel Adams and John Hancock," said Grandfather. "Yet they were of the same

BENJAMIN FRANKLIN

side in politics, and had an equal agency in the Revolution. Hancock was born to the inheritance of the largest fortune in New England. His tastes and habits were aristocratic. He loved gorgeous attire, a splendid mansion, magnificent furniture, stately festivals, and all that was glittering and pompous in external things. His manners were so polished that there stood not a nobleman at the footstool of King George's throne, who was a more skillful courtier† than John Hancock might have been. Nevertheless, he, in his embroidered clothes, and Samuel Adams in his threadbare coat, wrought together in the cause of liberty. Adams acted from pure and rigid principle. Hancock, though he loved his country, yet thought quite as much of his own popularity as he did of the people's rights. It is remarkable that these two men, so very different as I describe them, were the only two exempted from pardon by the king's proclamation."‡

JAMES OTIS

On the next leaf of the book, was the portrait of General Joseph Warren. Charley recognized the name, and said that here was a greater man than either Hancock or Adams.

"Warren was an eloquent and able patriot," replied Grandfather. "He deserves a lasting memory for his zealous efforts in behalf of liberty. No man's voice was more powerful in Faneuil Hall than Joseph Warren's.‡ If his death had not happened so early in the contest, he would probably have gained a high name as a soldier."

JOSIAH QUINCY

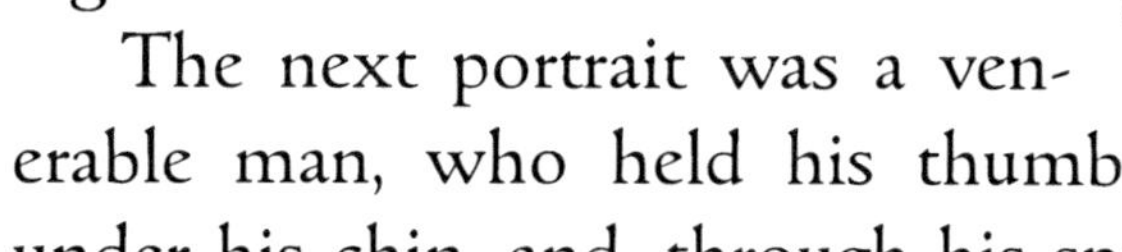

The next portrait was a venerable man, who held his thumb under his chin, and, through his spectacles, appeared to be attentively reading a manuscript.

"Here we see the most illustrious Boston boy that ever lived," said Grandfather. "This is Benjamin Franklin! But I will not try to compress, into a few sentences, the character of the sage, who, as a Frenchman expressed it, snatched the lightning from the sky, and the scepter from a tyrant. Mr. Sparks‡ must help you to the knowledge of Franklin."

JOHN ADAMS

The book likewise contained portraits of James Otis and Josiah Quincy. Both of them, Grandfather observed, were men of wonderful talents and true patriotism. Their voices were like the stirring tones of a trumpet, arousing the country to defend its freedom. Heaven seemed to have provided a greater number of eloquent men than had appeared at any other period, in order that the people might be fully instructed as to their wrongs, and the method of resistance.

"It is marvellous," said Grandfather, "to see how many powerful writers, orators, and soldiers started up, just at the time when they were wanted. There was a man for every kind of work. It is equally wonderful that men of such different characters were all made to unite in the one object of establishing the freedom and independence of America. There was an overruling Providence above them."

"Here was another great man," remarked Laurence, pointing to the portrait of John Adams.

"Yes; an earnest, warm-tempered, honest, and most able man," said Grandfather. "At the period of which we are now speaking, he was a lawyer in Boston. He was destined, in after years, to be ruler over the whole American people, whom he contributed so much to form into a nation."

Grandfather here remarked, that many a New Englander, who had passed his boyhood and youth in obscurity, afterward attained to a fortune, which he never could have foreseen, even in his most ambitious dreams. John Adams, the second president of the United States, and the equal of crowned kings, was once a schoolmaster and country lawyer. Hancock, the first signer of the Declaration of Independence, served his apprenticeship with a merchant. Samuel Adams, afterward governor of Massachusetts, was a small tradesman and a tax gatherer. General Warren was a physician, General Lincoln a farmer, and General Knox a bookbinder. General Nathaniel Greene, the best soldier, except

Washington, in the Revolutionary army, was a Quaker and a blacksmith. All these became illustrious men, and can never be forgotten in American history.

"And any boy, who is born in America, may look forward to the same things," said our ambitious friend Charley.

After these observations, Grandfather drew the book of portraits towards him, and showed the children several British peers and members of Parliament, who had exerted themselves either for or against the rights of America. There were the Earl of Bute, Mr. Grenville, and Lord North. These were looked upon as deadly enemies to our country.

Among the friends of America was Mr. Pitt, afterward Earl of Chatham, who spent so much of his wondrous eloquence in endeavoring to warn England of the consequences of her injustice. He fell down on the floor of the House of Lords, after uttering almost his dying words in defense of our privileges as freemen. There was Edmund Burke, one of the wisest men and greatest orators that ever the world produced. There was Colonel Barré, who had been among our fathers, and knew that they had courage enough to die for their rights. There was Charles James Fox, who never rested until he had silenced our enemies in the House of Commons.

"It is very remarkable to observe how many of the ablest orators in the British Parliament were favorable to America," said Grandfather. "We ought to remember these great Englishmen with gratitude; for their speeches encouraged our fathers, almost as much as those of our own orators, in Faneuil Hall, and under Liberty Tree. Opinions, which might have been received with doubt, if expressed only by a native

WILLIAM PITT

EDMUND BURKE

CHARLES JAMES FOX

FRIEND

American, were set down as true, beyond dispute, when they came from the lips of Chatham, Burke, Barré, or Fox."

"But, Grandfather," asked Laurence, "were there no able and eloquent men in this country who took the part of King George?"

"There were many men of talent, who said what they could in defense of the king's tyrannical proceedings," replied Grandfather. "But they had the worst side of the argument, and therefore seldom said anything worth remembering. Moreover their hearts were faint and feeble; for they felt that the people scorned and detested them. They had no friends, no defense, except in the bayonets of the British troops. A blight fell upon all their faculties, because they were contending against the rights of their own native land."

"What were the names of some of them?" inquired Charley.

"Governor Hutchinson, Chief Justice Oliver, Judge Auchmuty, the Reverend Mather Byles, and several other clergymen, were among the most noted loyalists," answered

Grandfather.

"I wish the people had tarred and feathered every man of them!" cried Charley.

"That wish is very wrong, Charley," said Grandfather. "You must not think that there was no integrity and honor, except among those who stood up for the freedom of America. For aught I know, there was quite as much of these qualities on one side as on the other. Do you see nothing admirable in a faithful adherence to an unpopular cause? Can you not respect that principle of loyalty, which made the royalists give up country, friends, fortune, every thing, rather than be false to their king? It was a mistaken principle; but many of them cherished it honorably, and were martyrs to it."

"Oh, I was wrong!" said Charley, ingenuously.† "And I would risk my life, rather than one of those good old royalists should be tarred and feathered."

"The time is now come, when we may judge fairly of them," continued Grandfather. "Be the good and true men among them honored; for

EARL OF BUTE

GEORGE GRENVILLE

LORD NORTH

FOE

they were as much our countrymen as the patriots were. And, thank Heaven! Our country need not be ashamed of her sons–of most of them, at least–whatever side they took in the Revolutionary contest."

Among the portraits was one of King George the Third.‡ Little Alice clapped her hands, and seemed pleased with the bluff good nature of his physiognomy.† But Laurence thought it strange that a man with such a face, indicating hardly a common share of intellect, should have had influence enough on human affairs, to convulse the world with war. Grandfather observed that this poor king had always appeared to him one of the most unfortunate persons that ever lived. He was so honest and conscientious, that if he had been only a private man, his life would probably have been blameless and happy. But his was that worst of fortunes, to be placed in a station far beyond his abilities.

"And so," said Grandfather, "his life, while he retained what intellect Heaven had gifted him with, was one long mortification. At last, he grew crazed with care and trouble. For nearly twenty years, the monarch of England was confined as a madman. In his old age, too, God took away his eyesight; so that his royal palace was nothing to him but a dark, lonesome prison house."

Chapter VII
The Tea Party and Lexington

"Our old chair," resumed Grandfather, "did not now stand in the midst of a gay circle of British officers. The troops, as I told you, had been removed to Castle William, immediately after the Boston Massacre. Still, however, there were many Tories, customhouse officers, and Englishmen, who used to assemble in the British Coffee House, and talk over the affairs of the period. Matters grew worse and worse; and in 1773, the people did a deed, which incensed the king and ministry more than any of their former doings."

Grandfather here described the affair, which is known by the name of the Boston Tea Party. The Americans, for some time past, had left off importing tea, on account of the oppressive tax. The East India Company, in London, had a large stock of tea on hand, which they had expected to sell to the Americans, but could find no market for it. But, after a while, the government persuaded this company of merchants to send the tea to America.

"How odd it is," observed Clara, "that the liberties of America should have had any thing to do with a cup of tea!"

Grandfather smiled, and proceeded with his narrative. When the people of Boston heard that several cargoes of tea were coming across the Atlantic, they held a great many meetings at Faneuil Hall, in the Old South Church, and under Liberty Tree. In the midst of their debates, three ships arrived in the harbor with the tea on board. The people spent more than a fortnight in consulting what should be done. At last, on the 16th of December, 1773, they demanded of Governor Hutchinson, that he should immediately send the ships back to England.

The governor replied that the ships must not leave the harbor, until the customhouse duties upon the tea should be paid. Now, the payment of these duties was the very thing against which the people had set their faces; because it was a tax, unjustly imposed upon America by the English government. Therefore, in the dusk of the evening, as soon as Governor Hutchinson's reply was received, an immense crowd hastened to Griffin's Wharf, where the tea ships lay. The place is now called Liverpool Wharf.

"When the crowd reached the wharf," said Grandfather, "they saw that a set of wild-looking figures were already on board of the ships. You would have imagined that the Indian warriors, of old times, had come back again; for they wore the Indian dress, and had their faces covered with red and black paint, like the Indians, when they go to war. These grim figures hoisted the tea chests on the decks of the vessels, broke them open, and threw all the contents into the harbor."

"Grandfather," said little Alice, "I suppose Indians don't love tea; else they would never waste it so."

"They were not real Indians, my child," answered Grandfather. "They were white men, in disguise; because a heavy

BOSTON TEA PARTY

punishment would have been inflicted on them, if the king's officers had found who they were. But it was never known. From that day to this, though the matter has been talked of by all the world, nobody can tell the names of those Indian figures. Some people say that there were very famous men among them, who afterwards became governors and generals. Whether this be true, I cannot tell."

When tidings of this bold deed were carried to England, King George was greatly enraged.‡ Parliament immediately passed an act, by which all vessels were forbidden to take in or discharge their cargoes at the port of Boston. In this way, they expected to ruin all the merchants, and starve the poor people, by depriving them of employment. At the same time, another act was passed, taking away many rights and privileges which had been granted in the charter of Massachusetts.

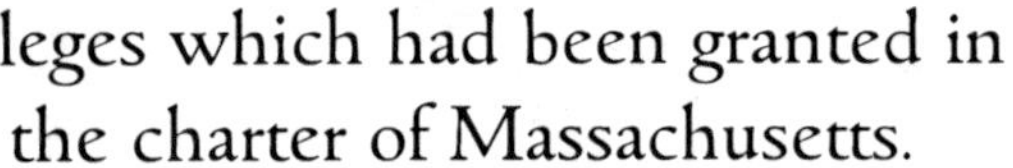

Governor Hutchinson, soon afterward, was summoned to England, in order that he might give his advice about the management of American affairs. General Gage, an officer of the Old French War, and since commander-in-chief of the British forces in America, was appointed governor in his stead. One of his first acts was to make Salem, instead of Boston, the metropolis of Massachusetts, by summoning the General Court to meet there.

According to Grandfather's description, this was the most gloomy time that Massachusetts had ever seen. The people groaned under as heavy a tyranny as in the days of Sir Edmund Andros. Boston looked as if it were afflicted with some dreadful pestilence,–so sad were the inhabitants, and so desolate the streets. There was no cheerful hum of business. The merchants shut up their warehouses, and the laboring men stood idle about the wharves. But all America felt interested in the good town of Boston; and contributions were raised, in many places, for the relief of the poor inhabitants.

"Our dear old chair!" exclaimed Clara. "How dismal it must have been now!"

"Oh," replied Grandfather, "a gay throng of officers had now come back to the British Coffee House; so that the old chair had no lack of mirthful company. Soon after General Gage became governor, a great many troops had arrived, and were encamped upon the Common. Boston was now a garrisoned and fortified town; for the general had built a battery across the neck, on the road to Roxbury, and placed guards for its defense. Every thing looked as if a civil war were close at hand."

"Did the people make ready to fight?" asked Charley.

"A Continental† Congress assembled at Philadelphia," said Grandfather, "and proposed such measures as they thought most conducive to the public good. A Provincial† Congress was likewise chosen in Massachusetts. They exhorted the people to arm and discipline themselves. A great number of minutemen were enrolled. The Americans called them minutemen, because they engaged to be ready to fight at a minute's warning. The English officers laughed, and said that the name was a very proper one, because the minutemen would run away the minute they saw the enemy. Whether they would fight or run, was soon to be proved."‡

Grandfather told the children that the first open resistance offered to the British troops, in the province of Massachusetts was at Salem. Colonel Timothy Pickering, with thirty or forty militia men, prevented the English colonel, Leslie, with four times as many regular soldiers, from taking possession of some military stores. No blood was shed on this occasion; but, soon afterward, it began to flow.

General Gage sent eight hundred soldiers to Concord, about eighteen miles from Boston, to destroy some ammunition and provisions which the colonists had collected there. They set out on their march in the evening of the 18th of April, 1775. The next morning, the General sent Lord Percy, with nine hundred men, to strengthen the troops which had gone before. All that day, the inhabitants of Boston heard various rumors. Some said that the British were making great slaughter among our countrymen. Others affirmed that every man had turned out with his musket, and that not a single soldier would ever get back to Boston.

"It was after sunset," continued Grandfather, "when the troops, who had marched forth so proudly, were seen entering Charlestown. They were covered with dust, and so hot and weary that their tongues hung out of their mouths. Many of them were faint with wounds. They had not all returned. Nearly three hundred were strewn, dead or dying, along the road from Concord. The yeomanry† had risen upon the invaders, and driven them back."

"Was this the battle of Lexington?" asked Charley.

"Yes," replied Grandfather; "it was so called, because the British, without provocation, had fired upon a party of minutemen, near Lexington meetinghouse, and killed eight of them. That fatal volley, which was fired by order of Major Pitcairn, began the war of the Revolution."‡

About this time, if Grandfather had been correctly informed, our chair disappeared from the British Coffee House. The manner of its departure cannot be satisfactorily ascertained. Perhaps the keeper of the Coffee House turned it out of doors, on account of its old-fashioned aspect. Perhaps he sold it as a curiosity. Perhaps it was taken, without leave, by some person who regarded it as public property, because it had once figured under Liberty Tree. Or, perhaps, the old chair, being of a peaceable disposition, had made use of its four oaken legs, and run away from the seat of war.

"It would have made a terrible clattering over the pavement," said Charley, laughing.

"Meanwhile," continued Grandfather, "during the mysterious non-appearance of our chair, an army of twenty thousand men had started up, and come to the siege of Boston. General Gage and his troops were cooped up within the narrow precincts of the peninsula. On the 17th of June, 1775, the famous battle of Bunker Hill was fought. Here General Warren fell. The British got the victory, indeed, but with the loss of more than a thousand officers and men."

"Oh, Grandfather," cried Charley, "you must tell us about that famous battle."

"No, Charley," said Grandfather, "I am not like other historians. Battles shall not hold a prominent place in the history of our quiet and comfortable old chair. But, tomorrow evening, Laurence, Clara, and yourself, and dear little Alice too, shall visit the Diorama of Bunker Hill.‡ There you shall see the whole business, the burning of Charlestown and all, with your own eyes, and hear the cannon and musketry with your own ears."

Chapter VIII
The Siege of Boston

The next evening but one, when the children had given Grandfather a full account of the Diorama of Bunker Hill, they entreated him not to keep them any longer in suspense about the fate of his chair. The reader will recollect that at the last accounts, it had trotted away upon its poor old legs, nobody knew whither. But, before gratifying their curiosity, Grandfather found it necessary to say something about public events.

The Continental Congress, which was assembled at Philadelphia, was composed of delegates from all the colonies. They had now appointed George Washington, of Virginia, to be commander-in-chief of all the American armies. He was, at that time, a member of Congress, but immediately left Philadelphia, and began his journey to Massachusetts. On the third of July, 1775, he arrived at Cambridge, and took command of the troops which were besieging General Gage.

"Oh, Grandfather," exclaimed Laurence, "it makes my heart throb to think what is coming now. We are to see General Washington himself."

The children crowded around Grandfather, and looked earnestly into his face. Even little Alice opened her sweet blue eyes, with her lips apart, and almost held her breath to listen; so instinctive is the reverence of childhood for the father of his country. Grandfather paused a moment; for he felt as if it might be irreverent to introduce the hallowed shade of Washington into a history, where an ancient elbow chair occupied the most prominent place. However, he determined to proceed with his narrative, and speak of the hero when it was needful, but with an unambitious simplicity.

So Grandfather told his auditors, that on General Washington's arrival at Cambridge, his first care was to reconnoitre† the British troops with his spyglass, and to examine the condition of his own army. He found that the American troops amounted to about fourteen thousand men. They were extended all round the peninsula of Boston, a space of twelve miles, from the high grounds of Roxbury on the right, to Mystic River on the left. Some were living in tents of sailcloth, some in shanties, rudely constructed of boards, some in huts of stone or turf, with curious windows and doors of basketwork.

WASHINGTON HEADQUARTERS

In order to be near the center, and oversee the whole of this wide-stretched army, the commander-in-chief made his headquarters at Cambridge, about half a mile from the colleges. A mansion-house, which perhaps had been the country seat of some Tory gentleman, was provided for his residence.

"When General Washington first entered this mansion," said Grandfather, "he was ushered up the staircase, and shown into a handsome apartment. He sat down in a large chair, which was the most conspicuous object in the room. The noble figure of Washington would have done honor to a throne. As he sat there, with his hand resting on the hilt of his sheathed sword, which was placed between his knees, his whole aspect well befitted the chosen man on whom his country leaned for the defense of her dearest rights. America seemed safe, under his protection. His face was grander than any sculptor had ever wrought in marble; none could behold him without awe and reverence. Never before had the lion's head, at the summit of the chair, looked down upon such a face and form as Washington's!"

"Why, Grandfather!" cried Clara, clasping her hands in amazement, "Was it really so? Did General Washington sit in our great chair?"

"I knew how it would be," said Laurence; "I foresaw it, the moment Grandfather began to speak."

Grandfather smiled. But, turning from the personal and domestic life of the illustrious leader, he spoke of the methods which Washington adopted to win back the metropolis of New England from the British.

The army, when he took command of it, was without any discipline or order. The privates considered themselves as good as their officers, and seldom thought it necessary to obey their commands, unless they understood the why and wherefore. Moreover, they were enlisted for so short a period, that, as soon as they began to be respectable soldiers, it was time to discharge them. Then came new recruits, who had to be taught their duty, before they could be of any service. Such was the army, with which Washington had to contend against more than twenty veteran British regiments.

Some of the men had no muskets, and almost all were without bayonets. Heavy cannon, for battering the British fortifications, were much wanted. There was but a small quantity of powder and ball, few tools to build entrenchments with, and a great deficiency of provisions and clothes for the soldiers. Yet, in spite of these perplexing difficulties, the eyes of the whole people were fixed on General Washington, expecting him to undertake some great enterprise against the hostile army.

The first thing that he found necessary, was to bring his own men into better order and discipline.‡ It is wonderful how soon he transformed this rough mob of country people into the semblance of a regular army. One of Washington's most invaluable characteristics, was the faculty of bringing order out of confusion. All business, with which he had any concern, seemed to regulate itself, as if by magic. The influence of his mind was like light, gleaming through an unshaped world. It was this faculty, more than any other, that made him so fit to ride upon the storm of the Revolution, when every thing was unfixed, and drifting about in a troubled sea.

"Washington had not been long at the head of the army," proceeded Grandfather, "before his soldiers thought as highly of him, as if he had led them to a hundred victories. They

GENERAL GEORGE WASHINGTON

knew that he was the very man whom the country needed, and the only one who could bring them safely through the great contest against the might of England. They put entire confidence in his courage, wisdom, and integrity†."

"And were not they eager to follow him against the British?" asked Charley.

"Doubtless they would have gone whithersoever his sword pointed the way," answered Grandfather; "and Washington was anxious to make a decisive assault upon the enemy. But as the enterprise was very hazardous, he called a council of all the generals in the army. Accordingly, they came from their different posts, and were ushered into the reception room. The commander-in-chief arose from our great chair to greet them."

WASHINGTON FIRING THE FIRST GUN AT YORKTOWN

"What were their names?" asked Charley.

"There was General Artemas Ward," replied Grandfather, "a lawyer by profession. He had commanded the troops before Washington's arrival. Another was General Charles Lee,‡ who had been a colonel in the English army, and was thought to possess vast military science. He came to the council, followed by two or three dogs, who were always at his heels. There was General Putnam, too, who was known all over New England by the name of Old Put."

"Was it he who killed the wolf?"‡ inquired Charley.

"The same," said Grandfather; "and he had done good service in the Old French War. His occupation was that of a farmer; but he left his plough in the furrow, at the news of Lexington battle. Then there was General Gates‡, who afterward gained great renown at Saratoga, and lost it again at Camden. General Greene‡, of Rhode Island, was likewise at the council. Washington soon discovered him to be one of the best officers in the army."

When the Generals were all assembled, Washington consulted them about a plan for storming the English batteries. But it was their unanimous opinion that so perilous an enterprise ought not to be attempted. The army, therefore, continued to besiege Boston, preventing the enemy from obtaining supplies of provisions, but without taking any immediate measures to get possession of the town. In this manner, the summer, autumn, and winter passed away.

"Many a night, doubtless," said Grandfather, "after Washington had been all day on horseback, galloping from one post of the army to another, he used to sit in our great chair, wrapped in earnest thought. Had you seen him, you might have supposed that his whole mind was fixed on the blue china tiles, which adorned the old fashioned fireplace. But, in reality, he was meditating how to capture the British army, or drive it out of Boston. Once, when there was a hard frost, he formed a scheme to cross the Charles River on the ice. But the other Generals could not be persuaded that there was any prospect of success."

"What were the British doing, all this time?" inquired Charley.

"They lay idle in the town," replied Grandfather. "General Gage had been recalled to England, and was succeeded by Sir William Howe. The British army, and the inhabitants of Boston, were now in great distress. Being shut up in the town so long, they had consumed almost all their provisions, and burnt up all their fuel. The soldiers tore down the Old North Church, and used its rotten boards and timbers for firewood. To heighten their distress, the smallpox broke out. They probably lost far more men by cold, hunger, and sickness, than had been slain at Lexington and Bunker Hill."

"What a dismal time for the poor women and children!" exclaimed Clara.

"At length," continued Grandfather, "in March, 1776, General Washington, who had now a good supply of powder, began a terrible cannonade and bombardment from Dorchester heights. One of the cannon balls which he fired into the town, struck the tower of the Brattle Street church, where it may still be seen. Sir William Howe made preparations to cross over in boats, and drive the Americans from their batteries, but was prevented by a violent gale and storm.‡ General Washington next erected a battery on Nook's Hill, so near the enemy, that it was impossible for them to remain in Boston any longer."

"Hurrah! Hurrah!" cried Charley, clapping his hands triumphantly. "I wish I had been there, to see how sheepish† the Englishmen looked."

And, as Grandfather thought that Boston had never witnessed a more interesting period than this, when the royal power was in its death agony, he determined to take a peep into the town, and imagine the feelings of those who were quitting it forever.

Chapter IX
The Tory's Farewell

"Alas for the poor Tories!" said Grandfather. "Until the very last morning after Washington's troops had shown themselves on Nook's Hill, these unfortunate persons could not believe that the audacious rebels, as they called the Americans, would ever prevail against King George's army. But, when they saw the British soldiers preparing to embark on board of the ships of war, then they knew that they had lost their country. Could the patriots have known how bitter were their regrets, they would have forgiven them all their evil deeds, and sent a blessing after them as they sailed away from their native shore."

In order to make the children sensible of the pitiable condition of these men, Grandfather singled out Peter Oliver,‡ chief justice of Massachusetts under the crown, and imagined him walking through the streets of Boston, on the morning before he left it forever.

This effort of Grandfather's fancy may be called–

The Tory's Farewell

Old Chief Justice Oliver threw on his red cloak, and placed his three-cornered hat on the top of his white wig. In this garb he intended to go forth and take a parting look at objects that had been familiar to him from his youth. Accordingly, he began his walk in the north part of the town, and soon came to Faneuil Hall. This edifice, the cradle of liberty, had been used by the British officers as a playhouse.

"Would that I could see its walls crumble to dust!" thought the chief justice; and, in the bitterness of his heart, he shook his fist at the famous hall. "There began the mischief which now threatens to rend asunder the British empire. The seditious† harangues of demagogues† in Faneuil Hall, have made rebels of a loyal people, and deprived me of my country."

He then passed through a narrow avenue, and found himself in King Street, almost in the very spot which, six years before, had been reddened by the blood of the Boston Massacre. The chief justice stepped cautiously, and shuddered, as if he were afraid that, even now, the gore of his slaughtered countrymen might stain his feet.

Before him rose the Town House, on the front of which were still displayed the royal arms. Within that edifice he had dispensed justice to the people, in the days when his name was never mentioned without honor. There, too, was the balcony whence the trumpet had been sounded, and the proclamation read to an assembled multitude, whenever a new king of England ascended the throne.

JUSTICE PETER OLIVER

"I remember–I remember," said Chief Justice Oliver to himself, "when his present most sacred Majesty was proclaimed. Then how the people shouted. Each man would have poured out his life-blood to keep a hair of King George's head from harm. But now, there is scarcely a tongue in all New England that does not imprecate† curses on his name. It is ruin and disgrace to love him. Can it be possible that a few fleeting years have wrought such a change!"

ESCORTING A TORY OUT OF TOWN

It did not occur to the chief justice that nothing but the most grievous tyranny could so soon have changed the people's hearts. Hurrying from the spot, he entered Cornhill, as the lower part of Washington Street was then called. Opposite to the Town House was the waste foundation of the Old North Church. The sacrilegious hands of the British soldiers had torn it down, and kindled their barrack fires with the fragments.

Further on, he

passed beneath the tower of the Old South. The threshold of this sacred edifice was worn by the iron tramp of horse's feet: for the interior had been used as a riding school and rendezvous for a regiment of dragoons†. As the chief justice lingered an instant at the door, a trumpet sounded within, and the regiment came clattering forth, and galloped down the street. They were proceeding to the place of embarkation.

"Let them go!" thought the chief justice, with somewhat of an old Puritan feeling in his breast. "No good can come of men who desecrate the house of God."

He went on a few steps further, and paused before the Province House. No range of brick stores had then sprung up to hide the mansion of the royal governors from public view. It had a spacious courtyard, bordered with trees, and enclosed with a wrought iron fence. On the cupola that surmounted the edifice was the gilded figure of an Indian chief, ready to let fly an arrow from his bow. Over the wide front door was a balcony, in which the chief justice had often stood, when the governor and high officers of the province showed themselves to the people.

While Chief Justice Oliver gazed sadly at the Province House, before which a sentinel was pacing, the double leaves of the door were thrown open, and Sir William Howe‡ made his appearance. Behind him came a throng of officers, whose steel scabbards† clattered against the stones, as they hastened down the courtyard. Sir William Howe was a dark-complexioned man, stern and haughty in his deportment. He stepped as proudly, in that hour of defeat, as if he were going to receive the submission of the rebel general.

The chief justice bowed and accosted him.

"This is a grievous hour for both of us, Sir William," said he.

"Forward, gentlemen!" said Sir William Howe to the officers who attended him. "We have no time to hear lamentations now!"

And, coldly bowing, he departed. Thus, the chief justice had a foretaste of the mortifications which the exiled New Englanders afterwards suffered from the haughty Britons. They were despised even by that country which they had served more faithfully than their own.

A still heavier trial awaited Chief Justice Oliver, as he passed onward from the Province House. He was recognized by the people in the street. They had long known him as the descendant of an ancient and honorable family. They had seen him sitting, in his scarlet robes, upon the judgment seat. All his life long, either for the sake of his ancestors, or on account of his own dignified station and unspotted character, he had been held in high respect. The old gentry of the province were looked upon almost as noblemen, while Massachusetts was under royal government.

But now, all hereditary reverence for birth and rank was gone. The inhabitants shouted in derision when they saw the venerable form of the old chief justice. They laid the wrongs of the country and their own sufferings during the siege–their hunger, cold, and sickness–partly to his charge and to that of his brother Andrew and his kinsman Hutchinson. It was by their advice that the king had acted in all the colonial troubles. But the day of recompense was come.

"See the old Tory!" cried the people, with bitter laughter.

A TORY'S DAY OF JUDGEMENT

"He is taking his last look at us. Let him show his white wig among us an hour hence, and we'll give him a coat of tar and feathers!"

The chief justice, however, knew that he need fear no violence, so long as the British troops were in possession of the town. But, alas! It was a bitter thought that he should leave no loving memory behind him. His forefathers, long after their spirits left the earth, had been honored in the affectionate remembrance of the people. But he, who would henceforth be dead to his native land, would have no epitaph† save scornful and vindictive words. The old man wept.

"They curse me–they invoke all kinds of evil on my head!" thought he, in the midst of his tears. "But, if they could read my heart, they would know that I love New England well. Heaven bless her, and bring her again under the rule of our gracious king! A blessing, too, on these poor, misguided people!"

The chief justice flung out his hands with a gesture, as if he were bestowing a parting benediction on his countrymen. He had now reached the southern portion of the town, and was far within the range of cannon shot from the American batteries. Close beside him was the broad stump of a tree, which appeared to have been recently cut down. Being weary and heavy at heart, he was about to sit down upon the stump.

Suddenly, it flashed upon his recollection, that this was the stump of Liberty Tree!‡ The British soldiers had cut it down, vainly boasting that they could as easily overthrow the liberties of America. Under its shadowy branches, ten years before, the brother of Chief Justice Oliver had been compelled to acknowledge the supremacy of the people by taking the oath which they prescribed. This tree was connected with all the events that had severed America from England.

"Accursed tree!" cried the chief justice, gnashing his teeth: for anger overcame his sorrow. "Would that thou hadst been left standing, till Hancock, Adams, and every other traitor, were hanged upon thy branches! Then fitly mightest thou have been hewn down, and cast into the flames."

He turned back, hurried to Long Wharf without looking behind him, embarked with the British troops for Halifax, and never saw his country more. Throughout the remainder of his days, Chief Justice Oliver was agitated with those same conflicting emotions that had tortured him while taking his farewell walk through the streets of Boston. Deep love and fierce resentment burned in one flame within his breast. Anathemas† struggled with benedictions†. He felt as if one breath of his native air would renew his life, yet would have died, rather than breathe the same air with rebels.

And such, likewise, were the feelings of the other exiles, a thousand in number, who departed with the British army. Were they not the most unfortunate of men?

***

"The misfortunes of these exiled Tories," observed Laurence, "must have made them think of the poor exiles of Acadia."

"They had a sad time of it, I suppose," said Charley. "But I choose to rejoice with the patriots, rather than be sorrowful with the Tories. Grandfather, what did General Washington do now?"

"As the rear of the British army embarked from the wharf," replied Grandfather, "General Washington's troops marched over the neck, through the fortification gates, and entered Boston in triumph. And now, for the first time since the pilgrims landed, Massachusetts was free from the dominion of England. May she never again be subjected to foreign rule–never again feel the rod of oppression!"

"Dear Grandfather," asked little Alice, "did General Washington bring our chair back to Boston?"

"I know not how long the chair remained at Cambridge," said Grandfather. "Had it stayed there till this time, it could not have found a better or more appropriate shelter. The mansion which General Washington occupied is still standing; and his apartments have since been tenanted by several eminent men. Governor Everett, while a professor in the university, resided there. So at an after period, did Mr. Sparks,‡ whose invaluable labors have connected his name with the immortality of Washington. And, at this very time, a venerable friend and contemporary of your Grandfather, after long pilgrimages beyond the sea, has set up his staff of rest at Washington's headquarters."

"You mean Professor Longfellow,‡ Grandfather," said Laurence. "Oh, how I should love to see the author of those beautiful *Voices of the Night!*"

"We will visit him next summer," answered Grandfather, "and take Clara and little Alice with us–and Charley, too, if he will be quiet."

Chapter X
The War for Independence

When Grandfather resumed his narrative, the next evening, he told the children that he had some difficulty in tracing the movements of the chair, during a short period after General Washington's departure from Cambridge.

Within a few months, however, it made its appearance at a shop in Boston, before the door of which was seen a striped pole. In the interior was displayed a stuffed alligator, a rattlesnake's skin, a bundle of Indian arrows, an old-fashioned matchlock† gun, a walking stick of Governor Winthrop's, a wig of old Cotton Mather's, and a colored print of the Boston Massacre. In short, it was a barber's shop, kept by a Mr. Pierce,‡ who prided himself on having shaved General Washington, Old Put, and many other famous persons.

"This was not a very dignified situation for our venerable chair," continued Grandfather; "but, you know, there is no better place for news than a barber's shop. All the events of the Revolutionary War were heard of there, sooner than anywhere else. People used to sit in the chair, reading the newspaper or talking, and waiting to be shaved, while Mr. Pierce with his scissors and razor, was at work upon the heads or chins of his other customers."

"I am sorry the chair could not betake itself to some

more suitable place of refuge," said Laurence. "It was old now, and must have longed for quiet. Besides, after it had held Washington in its arms, it ought not to have been compelled to receive all the world. It should have been put into the pulpit of the Old South Church, or some other consecrated place."

"Perhaps so," answered Grandfather. "But the chair, in the course of its varied existence, had grown so accustomed to general intercourse with society, that I doubt whether it would have contented itself in the pulpit of the Old South. There it would have stood solitary, or with no livelier companion than the silent organ, in the opposite gallery, six days out of seven. I incline to think that it had seldom been situated more to its mind, than on the sanded floor of the snug little barber's shop."

Then Grandfather amused his children and himself, with fancying all the different sorts of people who had occupied our chair while they awaited the leisure of the barber.

There was the old clergyman, such as Dr. Chauncey,‡ wearing a white wig, which the barber took from his head, and placed upon a wig block. Half an hour, perhaps, was spent in combing and powdering this reverend appendage to a clerical skull. There, too, were officers of the Continental army, who required their hair to be pomatumed† and plastered, so as to give them a bold and martial aspect. There, once in a while, was seen the thin, careworn, melancholy visage of an old Tory, with a wig that, in times long past, had perhaps figured at a Province House ball. And there, not infrequently, sat the rough captain of a privateer,† just returned from a successful cruise, in which he had captured

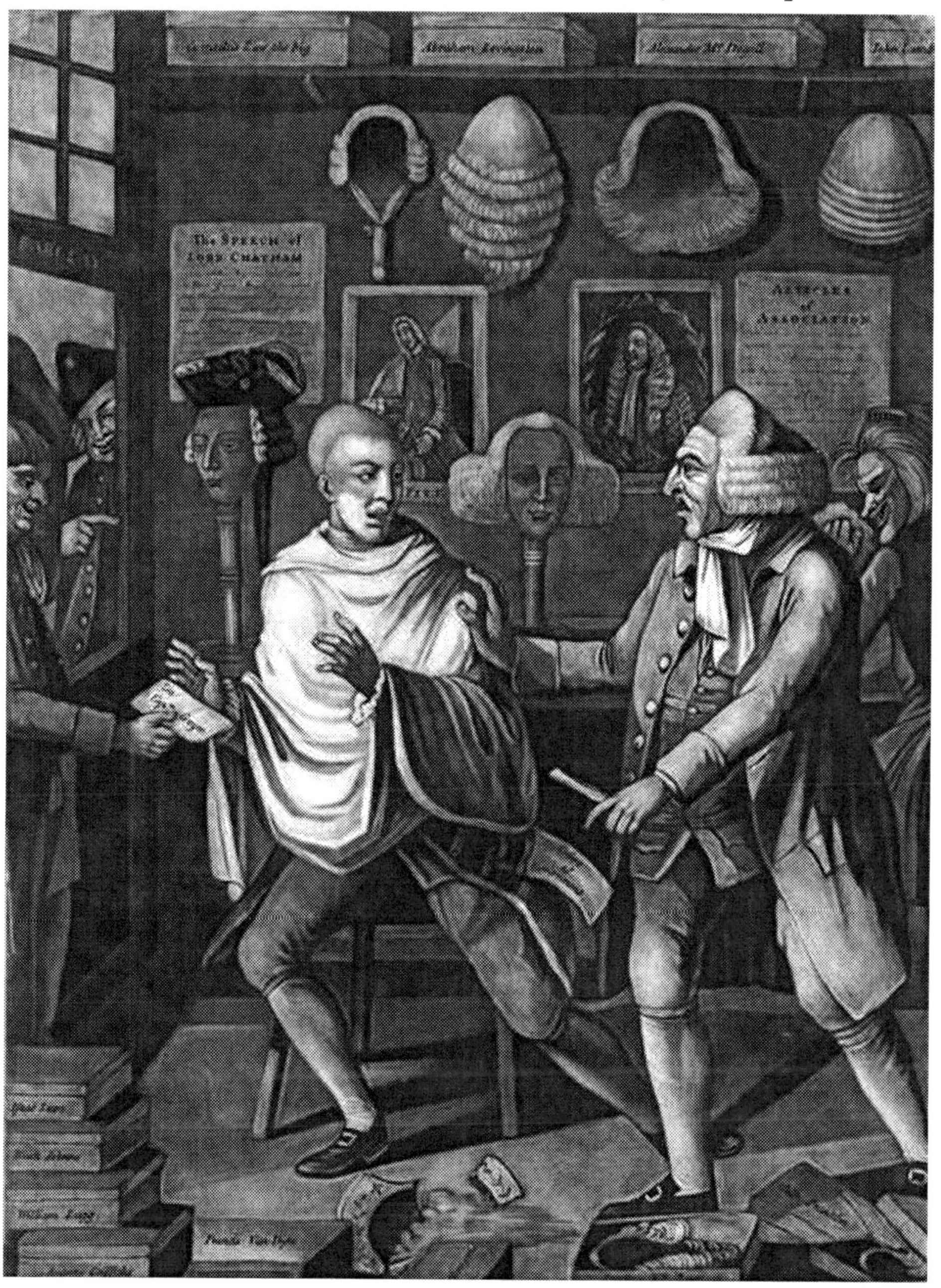

A PATRIOTIC BARBER

half a dozen richly laden vessels, belonging to King George's subjects. And sometimes a rosy little schoolboy climbed

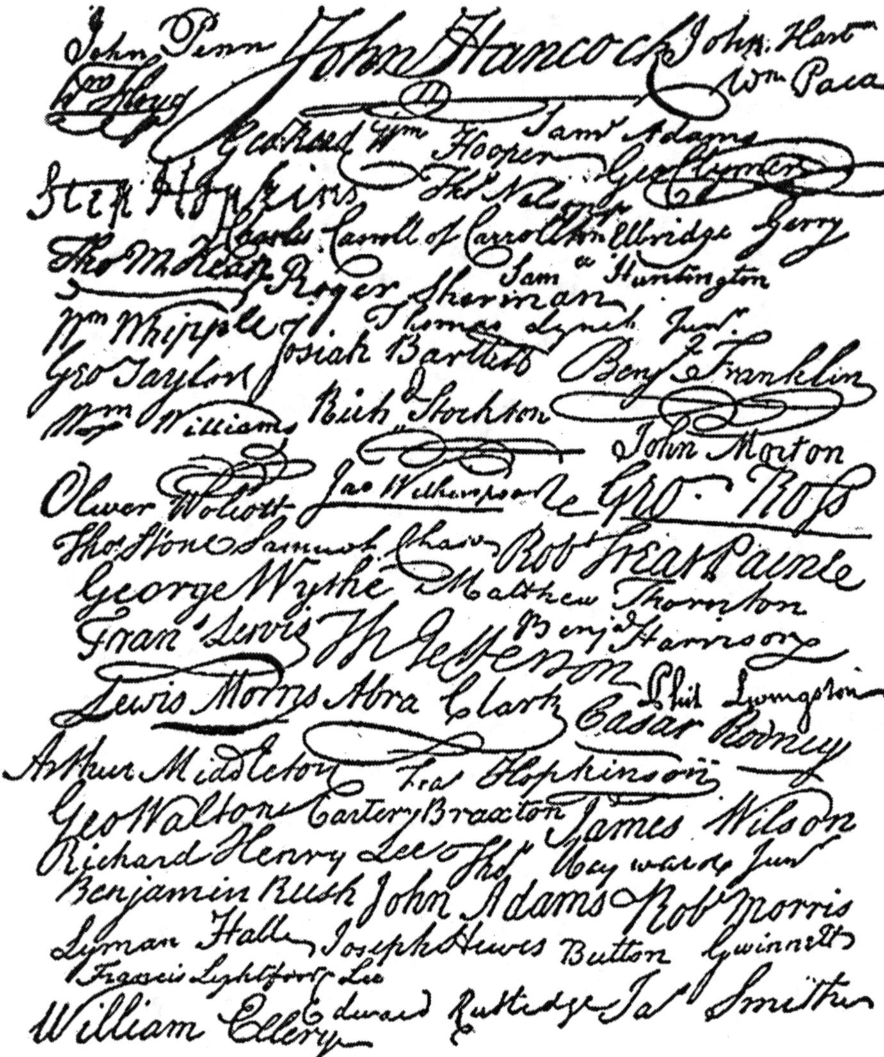

SIGNERS OF THE DECLARATION OF INDEPENDENCE

into our chair, and sat staring, with wide-open eyes, at the alligator, the rattlesnake, and the other curiosities of the barber's shop. His mother had sent him, with sixpence in his hand, to get his glossy curls cropped off. The incidents of the Revolution plentifully supplied the barber's customers with topics of conversation. They talked sorrowfully of the death of General Montgomery,‡ and the failure of our troops to take Quebec; for the New Englanders were now as anxious to get Canada from the English, as they had formerly been to conquer it from the French.

"But, very soon," said Grandfather, "came news from Philadelphia, the most important that America had ever heard of. On the 4th of July, 1776, Congress had signed the Declaration of Independence. The thirteen colonies were now free and independent states. Dark as our prospects were, the inhabitants welcomed these glorious tidings, and resolved to perish rather than again bear the yoke of England!"

"And I would perish too!" cried Charley.

"It was a great day–a glorious deed!" said Laurence, coloring high with enthusiasm. "And, Grandfather, I love to think that the sages in Congress showed themselves as bold and true as the soldiers in the field. For it must have required more courage to sign the Declaration of Independence than to fight the enemy in battle."

Grandfather acquiesced† in Laurence's view of the matter. He then touched briefly and hastily upon the prominent events of the Revolution. The thunderstorm of war had now rolled southward, and did not again burst upon Massachusetts, where its first fury had been felt. But she contributed her full share to the success of the contest. Wherever a battle was fought–whether at Long Island, White Plains, Trenton, Princeton, Brandywine, or Germantown–some of her brave sons were found slain upon the field.

In October, 1777, General Burgoyne surrendered his army at Saratoga,‡ to the American general, Gates. The captured troops were sent to Massachusetts. Not long afterwards,

Doctor Franklin and other American commissioners made a treaty at Paris, by which France bound herself to assist our countrymen. The gallant Lafayette was already fighting for our freedom, by the side of Washington. In 1778, a French fleet, commanded by Count d'Estaing, spent a considerable time in Boston Harbor. It marks the vicissitudes of human affairs, that the French, our ancient enemies, should come hither as comrades and brethren, and that kindred England should be our foe.

"While the war was raging in the Middle and Southern States," proceeded Grandfather, "Massachusetts had leisure to settle a new constitution of government, instead of the royal charter. This was done in 1780. In the same year, John Hancock, who had been president of Congress, was chosen governor of the state. He was the first whom the people had elected, since the days of old Simon Bradstreet."

"But, Grandfather, who had been governor since the British were driven away?" inquired Laurence. "General Gage and Sir William Howe were the last whom you have told us of."

"There had been no governor for the last four years," replied Grandfather. "Massachusetts had been ruled by the legislature, to whom the people paid obedience of their own accord. It is one of the most remarkable circumstances in our history, that, when the charter government was overthrown by the war, no anarchy, nor the slightest confusion ensued. This was a great honor to the people. But now Hancock was proclaimed governor by sound of trumpet; and there was again a settled government."

Grandfather again adverted† to the progress of the war.

SHAY'S REBELLION

In 1781, General Greene drove the British from the Southern States. In October, of the same year, General Washington compelled Lord Cornwallis to surrender his army, at Yorktown, in Virginia. This was the last great event of the revolutionary contest. King George and his ministers perceived that all the might of England could not compel America to renew her allegiance to the crown. After a great deal of discussion, a treaty of peace was signed, in September, 1783.

"Now, at last," said Grandfather, "after weary years of war, the regiments of Massachusetts returned in peace to their families. Now, the stately and dignified leaders, such as General Lincoln and General Knox, with their powdered hair and their uniforms of blue and buff, were seen moving about the streets."

"And little boys ran after them, I suppose," remarked Charley; "and the grown people bowed respectfully."

"They deserved respect, for they were good men, as well as brave," answered Grandfather. "Now, too, the inferior officers and privates came home, to seek some peaceful occupation. Their friends remembered them as slender and smooth-cheeked young men; but they returned with the erect and rigid mien† of disciplined soldiers. Some hobbled on crutches and wooden legs; others had received wounds, which were still rankling in their breasts. Many, alas! had fallen in battle, and perhaps were left unburied on the bloody field."

"The country must have been sick of war," observed Laurence.

"One would have thought so," said Grandfather. "Yet only two or three years elapsed, before the folly of some misguided men caused another mustering of soldiers. This affair was called Shays' War,‡ because a Captain Shays was the chief leader of the insurgents."

"Oh Grandfather, don't let there be another war!" cried little Alice, piteously.

Grandfather comforted his dear little girl, by assuring her that there was no great mischief done. Shays' War‡ happened in the latter part of 1786, and the beginning of the following year. Its principal cause was the badness of the times. The State of Massachusetts, in its public capacity, was very much in debt. So, likewise, were many of the people. An insurrection took place, the object of which seems to have been to interrupt the course of law and get rid of debts and taxes.

James Bowdoin,‡ a good and able man, was now governor of Massachusetts. He sent General Lincoln, at the head of four thousand men, to put down the insurrection. This general, who had fought through several hard campaigns in the Revolution, managed matters like an old soldier, and totally defeated the rebels, at the expense of very little blood.

"There is but one more public event to be recorded in the history of our chair," proceeded Grandfather. "In the year 1794, Samuel Adams was elected governor of Massachusetts. I have told you what a distinguished patriot he was, and how much he resembled the stern old Puritans. Could the ancient freemen of Massachusetts, who lived in the days of the first charter, have arisen from their graves, they would probably have voted for Samuel Adams to be governor."

"Well, Grandfather, I hope he sat in our chair!" said Clara.

"He did," replied Grandfather. "He had long been in the habit of visiting the barber's shop, where our venerable chair, philosophically forgetful of its former dignities, had now spent nearly eighteen not uncomfortable years. Such a remarkable piece of furniture, so evidently a relic of long departed times, could not escape the notice of Samuel Adams. He made minute researches into its history, and ascertained what a succession of excellent and famous people had occupied it."

"How did he find it out?" asked Charley. "For I suppose the chair could not tell its own history."

"There used to be a vast collection of ancient letters and other documents in the tower of the old South Church," answered Grandfather. "Perhaps the history of our chair was contained among these. At all events, Samuel Adams appears to have been well acquainted with it. When he became governor, he felt that he could have no more honorable seat than that which had been the ancient Chair of State. He therefore purchased it for a trifle, and filled it worthily for three years, as governor of Massachusetts."

"And what next?" asked Charley.

"That is all," said Grandfather, heaving a sigh; for he could not help being a little sad at the thought that his stories must close here. "Samuel Adams‡ died in 1803, at the age of above threescore and ten. He was a great patriot, but a poor man. At his death, he left scarcely property enough to pay the expenses of his funeral. This precious chair, among his other effects, was sold at auction; and your Grandfather, who was then in the strength of his years, became the purchaser."

Laurence, with a mind full of thoughts that struggled for expression, but could find none, looked steadfastly at the chair.

He had now learned all its history, yet was not satisfied.

"Oh, how I wish that the chair could speak!" cried he. "After its long intercourse with mankind–after looking upon the world for ages–what lessons of golden wisdom it might utter! It might teach a private person how to lead a good and happy life–or a statesman how to make his country prosperous!"

Chapter XI
Grandfather's Dream

Grandfather was struck by Laurence's idea that the historic chair should utter a voice, and thus pour forth the collected wisdom of two centuries. The old gentleman had once possessed no inconsiderable share of fancy; and even now its fading sunshine occasionally glimmered among his more somber reflections.

As the history of the chair had exhausted all his facts, Grandfather determined to have recourse to fable. So, after warning the children that they must not mistake this story for a true one, he related what we shall call,–

Grandfather's Dream

Laurence and Clara, where were you last night? Where were you, Charley, and dear little Alice? You had all gone to rest, and left old Grandfather to meditate alone in his great chair. The lamp had grown so dim that its light hardly illuminated the alabaster shade. The wood fire had crumbled into heavy embers, among which the little flames danced, and quivered, and sported about, like fairies.

And here sat Grandfather, all by himself. He knew that it was bedtime; yet he could not help longing to hear your merry voices, or to hold a comfortable chat with some old friend; because then his pillow would be visited by pleasant dreams. But, as neither children nor friends were at hand, Grandfather leaned back in the great chair and closed his eyes, for the sake of meditating more profoundly.

And, when Grandfather's meditations had grown very profound indeed, he fancied that he heard a sound over his head, as if somebody were preparing to speak.

"Hem!" it said, in a dry, husky tone. "H-e-m! Hem!"

As Grandfather did not know that any person was in the room, he started up in great surprise, and peeped hither and thither, behind the chair, and into the recess by the fireside, and at the dark nook yonder, near the bookcase. Nobody could he see.

"Pooh!" said Grandfather to himself, "I must have been dreaming."

But, just as he was going to resume his seat, Grandfather happened to look at the great chair. The rays of firelight were flickering upon it in such a manner that it really seemed as if its oaken frame were all alive. What! Did it not move its elbow? There, too! It certainly lifted one of its ponderous† forelegs, as if it had a notion of drawing itself a little nearer to the fire. Meanwhile, the lion's head nodded at Grandfather, with as polite and sociable a look as a lion's visage, carved in oak, could possibly be expected to assume. Well, this is strange!

"Good evening, my old friend," said the dry and husky voice, now a little clearer than before. "We have been intimately acquainted so long that I think it high time we have a chat together."

Grandfather was looking straight at the lion's head, and could not be mistaken in supposing that it moved its lips. So here the mystery was all explained.

"I was not aware," said Grandfather, with a civil salutation to his oaken companion, "that you possessed the faculty of speech. Otherwise, I should often have been glad to converse with such a solid, useful, and substantial, if not brilliant member of society."

"Oh!" replied the ancient chair, in a quiet and easy tone, for it had now cleared its throat of the dust of ages. "I am naturally a silent and incommunicative sort of character. Once or twice, in the course of a century, I unclose my lips. When the gentle Lady Arbella departed this life, I uttered a groan. When the honest mint-master weighed his plump daughter against the pine tree shillings, I chuckled audibly at the joke. When old Simon Bradstreet took the place of the tyrant Andros, I joined in the general huzza,† and capered† upon my wooden legs, for joy. To be sure, the bystanders were so fully occupied with their own feelings that my sympathy was quite unnoticed."

"And have you often held a private chat with your friends?" asked Grandfather.

"Not often," answered the chair. "I once talked with Sir William Phips, and communicated my ideas about the witchcraft delusion. Cotton Mather had several conversations with me, and derived great benefit from my historical reminiscences. In the days of the Stamp Act, I whispered in the ear of Hutchinson, bidding him to remember what stock his countrymen were descended of, and to think whether the spirit of their forefathers had utterly departed from them.

The last man whom I favored with a colloquy,† was that stout old republican, Samuel Adams."

"And how happens it," inquired Grandfather, "that there is no record nor tradition of your conversational abilities? It is an uncommon thing to meet with a chair that can talk."

"Why, to tell you the truth," said the chair, giving itself a hitch nearer to the hearth, "I am not apt to choose the most suitable moments for unclosing my lips. Sometimes I have inconsiderately begun to speak, when my occupant, lolling back in my arms, was inclined to take an after-dinner nap. Or, perhaps, the impulse to talk may be felt at midnight, when the lamp burns dim, and the fire crumbles into decay, and the studious or thoughtful man finds that his brain is in a mist. Oftenest, I have unwisely uttered my wisdom in the ears of sick persons, when the inquietude of fever made them toss about, upon my cushion. And so it happens, that though my words make a pretty strong impression at the moment, yet my auditors invariably remember them only as a dream. I should not wonder if you, my excellent friend, were to do the same tomorrow morning."

"Nor I either," thought Grandfather to himself. However, he thanked this respectable old chair for beginning the conversation, and begged to know whether it had anything particular to communicate.

"I have been listening attentively to your narrative of my adventures," replied the chair, "and it must be owned that your correctness entitles you to be held up as a pattern to biographers. Nevertheless, there are a few omissions which I should be glad to see supplied. For instance, you make no mention of the good knight, Sir Richard Saltonstall,‡ nor of

FIRST PRAYER IN CONGRESS

the famous Hugh Peters,‡ nor of those old regicide† judges, Whalley, Goffe, and Dixwell.‡ Yet I have borne the weight of all these distinguished characters at one time or another."

Grandfather promised amendment, if ever he should have an opportunity to repeat his narrative. The good old chair, which still seemed to retain a due regard for outward appearance, then reminded him how long a time had passed since it had been provided with a new cushion. It likewise expressed the opinion that the oaken figures on its back would show to much better advantage by the aid of a little varnish.

"And I have had a complaint in this joint," continued the chair, endeavoring to lift one of its legs, "ever since Charley trundled his wheelbarrow against me."

"It shall be attended to," said Grandfather. "And now, venerable chair, I have a favor to solicit. During an existence of more than two centuries, you have had a familiar intercourse with men who were esteemed the wisest of their day. Doubtless, with your capacious† understanding, you have treasured up many an invaluable lesson of wisdom. You certainly have had time enough to guess the riddle of life. Tell us poor mortals, then, how we may be happy!"

The lion's head fixed its eyes thoughtfully upon the fire, and the whole chair assumed an aspect of deep meditation. Finally, it beckoned to Grandfather with its elbow, and made a step sideways towards him, as if it had a very important secret to communicate.

"As long as I have stood in the midst of human affairs," said the chair, with a very oracular† enunciation, "I have constantly observed that JUSTICE, TRUTH, and LOVE, are the chief ingredients of every happy life."

"Justice, Truth, and Love!" exclaimed Grandfather. "We need not exist two centuries to find out that these qualities are essential to our happiness. This is no secret. Every human being is born with the instinctive knowledge of it."

"Ah!" cried the chair, drawing back in surprise. "From what I have observed of the dealings of man with man, and nation with nation, I never should have suspected that they knew this all-important secret. And, with this eternal lesson written in your soul, do you ask me to sift new wisdom for you, out of my petty existence of two or three centuries?"

"But, my dear chair–" said Grandfather.

"Not a word more," interrupted the chair; "here I close my lips for the next hundred years. At the end of that period, if I shall have discovered any new precepts of happiness, better than what Heaven has already taught you, they shall assuredly be given to the world."

In the energy of its utterance, the oaken chair seemed to stamp its foot, and trod (we hope unintentionally) upon Grandfather's toe. The old gentleman started, and found that he had been asleep in the great chair, and that his heavy walking stick had fallen down across his foot.

***

"Grandfather," cried little Alice, clapping her hands, "you must dream a new dream every night about our chair!"

Laurence, and Clara, and Charley said the same. But the good old gentleman shook his head, and declared that here ended the history, real or fabulous, of Grandfather's Chair.

Appendix III: A Letter from Governor Hutchinson

to Richard Jackson narrating the doings of the mob:

BOSTON, Aug. 30, 1765

MY DEAR SIR, -I came from my house at Milton, the 26 in the morning. After dinner it was whispered in town there would be a mob at night, and that Paxton, Hallowell, the customhouse, and admiralty officers' houses would be attacked; but my friends assured me that the rabble† were satisfied with the insult I had received and that I was become rather popular. In the evening, whilst I was at supper and my children round me, somebody ran in and said the mob were coming. I directed my children to fly to a secure place, and shut up my house as I had done before, intending not to quit it; but my eldest daughter repented† her leaving me, hastened back, and protested she would not quit the house unless I did. I couldn't stand against this, and withdrew with her to a neighboring house, where I had been but a few minutes before the hellish crew fell upon my house with the rage of devils, and in a moment with axes split down the doors and entered. My son being in the great entry heard them cry: "Damn him, he is upstairs, we'll have him." Some ran immediately as high as the top of the house, others filled the rooms below and cellars, and others remained without the house to be employed there. Messages soon came one after another to the house where

I was, to inform me the mob were coming in pursuit of me, and I was obliged to retire through yards and gardens to a house more remote, where I remained until 4 o'clock, by which time one of the best finished houses in the Province had nothing remaining but the bare walls and floors. Not contented with tearing off all the wainscot† and hangings, and splitting the doors to pieces, they beat down the partition walls; and although that alone cost them near two hours, they cut down the cupola or lanthorn,† and they began to take the slate and boards from the roof, and were prevented only by the approaching daylight from a total demolition of the building. The garden house was laid flat, and all my trees, etc., broke down to the ground.

Such ruin was never seen in America. Besides my plate† and family pictures, household furniture of every kind, my own, my children's, and servants' apparel, they carried off about £900 sterling in money, and emptied the house of everything whatsoever, except a part of the kitchen furniture, not leaving a single book or paper in it, and have scattered or destroyed all the manuscripts and other papers I had been collecting for thirty years together, besides a great number of public papers in my custody. The evening being warm, I had undressed me and put on a thin camlet† surtout† over my waistcoat. The next morning, the weather being changed, I had not clothes enough in my possession to defend me from the cold, and was obliged to borrow from my friends. Many articles of clothing and a good part of my plate have since been picked up in different quarters of the town, but the furniture in general was cut to pieces before it was thrown out of the house, and most of the beds cut open, and the feathers thrown out of the windows. The next evening, I intended with my children to Milton, but meeting two or three small parties of the ruffians, who I suppose had concealed themselves in the country, and my coachman hearing one of them say, "There he is!" My daughters were terrified and said they should never be safe, and I was forced to shelter them that night at the Castle.

The encouragers of the first mob never intended matters should go this length, and the people in general expressed the utter detestation† of this unparalleled outrage, and I wish they could be convinced what infinite hazard there is of the most terrible consequences from such demons, when they are let loose in a government where there is not constant authority at hand sufficient to suppress them. I am told the government here will make me a compensation for my own and my family's loss, which I think cannot be much less than £3,000 sterling. I am not sure that they will. If they should not, it will be too heavy for me, and I must humbly apply to his majesty in whose service I am a sufferer; but this, and a much greater sum would be an insufficient compensation for the constant distress and anxiety of mind I have felt for some time past, and must feel for months to come. You cannot conceive the wretched state we are in. Such is the resentment of the people against the Stamp-Duty, that there can be no dependence upon the General Court to take any steps to enforce, or rather advise, to the payment of it. On the other hand, such will be the effects of not submitting to it, that all trade must cease, all courts fall, and all authority be at an end. Must not the ministry be excessively embarrassed? On the one hand, it will be said, if concessions† are made, the Parliament endanger the loss of their authority over the Colony: on the other hand, if external forces should be used, there seems to be danger of a total lasting alienation of affection. Is there no alternative? May the infinitely wise God direct you.

Edgewater Brief

the
'Story within the Story'

EDGEWATER BRIEF

Dear Parents, Teachers, and other Curious Readers,

It is our pleasure to present this annotated edition of a classic history for young people. A '†' next to a word indicates a definition from Webster's 1828 dictionary for the form of the word related to the text. For instance, if the word is used as a noun but has a verb form, the noun definition is given. We've chosen those definitions best reflecting the context in which the word is used.

A '‡' next to a word or at the end of a sentence indicates an explanation or elaboration from another text. By clarifying the author's references and asides, we give you the 'story within the story'. Try keeping a bookmark back here to mark the part of the brief that corresponds to your place in the text.

Page 16

†**AUD'ITOR**, [L.] A hearer; one who attends to hear a discourse.

Page 17

†**SENSIBIL'ITY**, n. 1. Capacity of acuteness of perception; that quality of the soul which renders it susceptible of impressions; delicacy of feeling; as *sensibility* to pleasure or pain; *sensibility* to shame or praise; exquisite *sensibility*.

†**VEN'ERABLE**, a. [L. venerabilis, from veneror, to honor, to worship.] Worthy of veneration or reverence; deserving of honor and respect; as a *venerable* magistrate.

Page 19

†**PU'RITAN**, n. [from pure.] A dissenter from the church of England. The Puritans were so called in derision, on account of their professing to follow the pure word of God, in opposition to all traditions and human constitutions. [Author David] Hume gives this name to three parties; the political Puritans, who maintained the highest principles of civil liberty; the Puritans in discipline, who were averse to the ceremonies and government of the Episcopal church; and the doctrinal Puritans, who rigidly defended the speculative system of the first reformers.

Page 20

†**CHARTER**, n. A written instrument, executed with usual forms, given as evidence of a grant, contract, or whatever is done between man and man. In its more usual sense, it is the instrument of a grant conferring powers, rights and privileges, either from a king or other sovereign power, or from a private person, as a charter of exemption, that no person shall be empaneled on a jury, a charter of pardon, &c. The charters under which most of the colonies in America were settled, were given by the king of England, and incorporated certain persons, with powers to hold the lands granted, to establish a government, and make laws for their own regulation. These were called charter-governments. 2. Any instrument, executed with form and solemnity, bestowing rights or privileges.

Page 23

†'**ASPECT**, n. [L. 'aspectus, from aspicio, to look on, of ad and specio, to see or look.] Countenance; look, or particular appearance of the face; as a mild or severe *aspect*.

Page 24

†**RUDE**, a. [L. rudis. The sense is probably rough, broken, and this word may be allied to raw and crude.] 1. rough; uneven; rugged; unformed by art; as *rude* workmanship, that is, roughly finished; *rude* and unpolished stones. 2. Rough; of coarse manners; unpolished; uncivil; clownish; rustic; as a *rude* countryman; *rude* behavior; *rude* treatment; a *rude* attack. 3. Artless; inelegant; not polished; as a *rude* translation of Virgil.

Page 25

†**SAGAMORE**, n. Among some tribes of American Indians, a king or chief.

Page 26

†**PIKE**, n. [This word belongs to a numerous family of words expressing something pointed, or a sharp point, or as verbs, to dart, to thrust, to prick.] A military weapon consisting of a long wooden shaft or staff, with a flat steel head pointed; called the spear. This weapon was formerly used by infantry, but its use is now limited to officers, and it is called a sponton or spontoon. Its use among soldiers is superseded by the bayonet.

Page 27

†**MULTIFA'RIOUS**, a. [L. multifarius.] Having great multiplicity; having great diversity or variety; as *multifarious* artifice.

Page 28

†**STICK, WALKING-STAFF, WALKING-STICK**, n. A staff or stick carried in the hand for support or amusement in walking.

Page 31

†**RECESS'**, n. [L. recessus, from recedo.] 1. Place of retirement or secrecy; private abode. 2. Privacy; seclusion from the world or from company.

‡**MONUMENT**; "As early as 1776, some steps were taken toward the commemoration of the battle of **Bunker Hill** and the fall of General Warren, who was buried upon the hill the day after the action...[The plans, for the most part, remained unrealized, but]...as the half-century from the date of the battle drew toward a close, a stronger feeling of the duty of commemorating it began to be awakened in the community...[The laying of the cornerstone was a celebration] unequalled in magnificence by any thing of the kind that had been seen in New England. The morning proved propitious. The air was cool, the sky was clear, and timely showers the previous day had brightened the vesture of nature into its loveliest hue. Delighted thousands flocked into Boston to bear a part in the proceedings, or to witness the spectacle. At about ten o'clock a procession moved from the State House towards Bunker Hill. The military, in their fine uniforms, formed the van. About two hundred veterans of the Revolution, of whom forty were survivors of the battle [of Bunker Hill], rode in barouches next to the escort. These venerable men, the relics of a past generation, with emaciated frames, tottering limbs, and trembling voices, constituted a touching spectacle. Some wore, as honorable decora-

tions, their old fighting equipment, and some bore the scars of still more honorable wounds. Glistening eyes constituted their answer to the enthusiastic cheers of the grateful multitudes who lined their pathway and cheered their progress. To this patriot band succeeded the Bunker Hill Monument Association. Then the Masonic fraternity, in their splendid regalia, thousands in number. Then [General] Lafayette, continually welcomed by tokens of love and gratitude, and the invited guests. Then a long array of societies, with their various badges and banners. It was a splendid procession, and of such length that the front nearly reached Charlestown Bridge ere the rear had left Boston Common. It proceeded to Breed's Hill, where the Grand Master of the Freemasons, the President of the Monument Association, and General Lafayette, performed the ceremony of laying the corner-stone, in the presence of a vast concourse of people...[An] address was delivered by Mr. [Daniel] Webster, in the presence of as great a multitude as was ever perhaps assembled within the sound of a human voice." (Source: Edwin P. Whipple and Richard Frothingham, Jr., *The Great Speeches and Orations of Daniel Webster*)

Page 32

‡**OLIVER CROMWELL**; Called "Old Ironsides", **Oliver Cromwell** was a brilliant, though controversial, English military leader during the civil wars that marked the tumultuous reign of **Charles I**. After the death of King Charles he took control of England, becoming **Lord Protector** of England, Scotland and Ireland, and of the American colonies. A staunch Puritan,"...that which chiefly distinguished the army of Cromwell from other armies was the austere morality and the fear of God which pervaded all ranks. It is acknowledged by the most zealous royalists that, in that singular camp, no oath was heard, no drunkenness or gambling was seen, and that, during the long dominion of the soldiery, the property of the peaceable citizen and the honor of woman were held sacred. If outrages were committed, they were outrages of a very different kind from those of which a victorious army is generally guilty. No servant girl complained of the rough gallantry of the redcoats. Not an ounce of plate was taken from the shops of the goldsmiths. But a Pelagian sermon, or a window on which the Virgin and Child were painted, produced in the Puritan ranks an excitement which it required the utmost exertions of the officers to quell. One of Cromwell's chief difficulties was to restrain the pikemen and dragoons from invading by main force the pulpits of ministers whose discourses, to use the language of that time, were not savory; and too many of our cathedrals still bear the marks of the hatred with which those stern spirits regarded every vestige of Popery." (Source: Thomas Macauley, *History of England*, Volume I)

For a short biographical sketch of Oliver Cromwell, see *Biographical Stories* by Nathaniel Hawthorne.

Page 33

†**ABSTRU'SE,** a. [L. abstrusus, from abstrudo, to thrust away, to conceal; abs and trudo; Eng. to thrust.] Hid; concealed; hence, remote from apprehension; difficult to be comprehended or understood; opposed to what is obvious. [Not used of material objects.]

Page 34

†**TEM'PORAL**, a. [L. temporalis, from tempus, time.] Pertaining to this life or this world or the body only; secular; as temporal concerns; temporal affairs. In this sense, it is opposed to spiritual. Let not *temporal* affairs or employments divert the mind from spiritual concerns, which are far more important.

†**PO'PISH**, a. Relating to the pope; taught by the pope; pertaining to the pope or to the church of Rome; as *popish* tenets or ceremonies.

†**PAPIS'TICAL**, a. Popish; pertaining to popery; adherent to the church of Rome and its doctrines and ceremonies.

Page 35

†**GORG'ET**, n. A piece of armor for defending the throat or neck; a kind of breast-plate like a half-moon; also, a small convex ornament worn by officers on the breast.

Page 37

‡**KING CHARLES THE FIRST**; "Baby Charles became King Charles I, in the twenty-fifth year of his age. Unlike his father [**James the First**], he was usually amiable in his private character, and grave and dignified in his bearing; but, like his father, he had monstrously exaggerated notions of the rights of a king, and was evasive, not to be trusted...Now you are to understand that King Charles the First–of his own determination to be a high and mighty King not to be called to account by anybody, and urged on by his Queen besides–deliberately set himself to put his Parliament down and to put himself up. You are also to understand, that even in pursuit of this wrong idea (enough in itself to have ruined any king) he never took a straight course, but always took a crooked one." (Source: Charles Dickens, *A Child's History of England*)

"**Charles I**...being very much of a Scot...had also the virtue of a Scot, courage, and a quite natural dignity, and an appetite for the things of the mind. Being somewhat Scottish, he was very un-English, and could not manage a compromise: he tried instead to split hairs, and seemed merely to break promises. Yet he might safely have been far more inconsistent if he had been a little hearty and hazy; but he was of the sort that sees everything in black and white; and it is therefore remembered–especially the black. From the first he fenced with his Parliament as with a mere foe...His minister, the great Strafford, was foiled in an attempt to make him strong in the fashion of a French king, and perished on the scaffold, a frustrated Richelieu. The Parliament claiming the power of the purse, Charles appealed to the power of the sword, and at first carried all before him; but success passed to the wealth of the Parliamentary class, the discipline of the new army, and the patience and genius of **Cromwell**; and Charles died the same death as his great servant." (Source: G. K. Chesterton, *A Short History of England*)

Page 38

‡**ROGER WILLIAMS BANK**; Thomas Jefferson was instrumental in starting the **Roger Williams Bank** in Providence, Rhode Island in 1803. In 1900, the bank became part of the Industrial Trust Company. (Source: Durand, Roger H., *Obsolete Notes and Scrip of Rhode Island and the Providence Plantations*.)

Page 43

†**POLEM'IC**, a. [Gr. war.] 1. Controversial; disputative; intended to maintain an opinion or system in opposition to others; as a polemic treatise, discourse, essay or book; polemic divinity. 2. Engaged in supporting an opinion or system by controversy; as a polemic writer.

‡**HISTORY OF ENGLAND**; Perhaps a reference to David Hume's *History of England.*

‡**VANE**; Reference to *Life of Sir Henry Vane*, by Charles W. Upham. Henry Vane, governor of Massachusetts for a year in 1636, became a member of the English parliament. After the civil wars and the restoration of the monarchy, Vane was convicted of treason and a "sentence of death was finally passed upon him. He was

condemned to be hanged, quartered, &c.; but owing to some cause, probably the influence of his great connections, the mode of death was commuted to beheading on Tower Hill...[Vane eloquently defended himself, and] as might have been expected, and as the government had most seriously apprehended, a great impression had by this time been made by the prisoner upon the vast multitude that surrounded him. The people remembered his career of inflexible virtue and patriotism ...The enthusiasm with which he had been welcomed by weeping and admiring thousands as he passed from prison to Tower Hill...his visible triumph over the fear of death and the malice of his enemies, all these influences, brought at once to bear upon their minds, and concentrated and heightened by the powers of an eloquence that was the wonder of his contemporaries, had produced an effect, which, it was evident, could not, with safety to the government, be permitted to be wrought any higher...the trumpets were...sounded [to drown out Vane's voice]. The sheriff attempted to catch a paper from his hands. Sir John Robinson, seeing some persons taking minutes of the speech, ordered their reports to be destroyed. Six notebooks were delivered up to the officers...The trumpets were again blown, and Sir John Robinson, with two or three others, rushed upon the prisoner and endeavored to seize his papers. He, however, kept them off from his person, and after a while, tearing the papers himself, handed the remnants to one of his friends, from whom they were forcibly taken. The officers then attempted to thrust their hands into the prisoner's pockets, and a scene of disorder and brutal violence occurred upon the scaffold...Finding that it was determined that he should not be heard, and unwilling to have the few moments of life that remained broken in upon by such disagreeable incidents, he desisted from all further attempts to address the people, merely remarking, 'It is a bad cause which cannot bear the words of a dying man.'" (Source: Charles W. Upham, *Life of Sir Henry Vane*)

Page 44

‡**[THOMAS] HOOKER**; The colonial founder of Hartford, Connecticut. "**Governor Winthrop** and followers did not believe that all people were wise enough to take part in the affairs of government. They believed in the rule of a select few...Others, led by Rev. Thomas Hooker, believed that all persons should have a voice in the government. Their views were well expressed by Hooker: 'In matters which concern the good, a general council, chosen by all to transact business which concerns all, I conceive most suitable to rule.' These different views were among the reasons which led Hooker to seek a new home and plant a new colony." (Source: E. G. Foster, *A History of the United States*)

‡**[JOHN] DAVENPORT**; The founder of New Haven, Connecticut "...had been actively concerned in obtaining the patent of the Massachusetts Colony, and had contributed both money and time in its aid. A favorable account of the success of the colony having reached him, he sailed on the *Hector*, reaching Boston on 26 June, 1637. He was heartily welcomed, and was regarded as an important aid in sustaining the interests of religion. During August of the same year he sat with the famous synod of Cambridge. In March 1638, with many of the families that had accompanied him from England, he sailed from Boston to Quinipine, which they afterward named New Haven. The party reached their new home on 14 April and on the following day, which was the Sabbath, Mr. Davenport preached under the branches of a large oak on 'The Temptations of the Wilderness.'" (Source: *Appleton's Cyclopedia of American Biography*)

Page 47

†**HOUSE [OF REPRESENTATIVES]**, n. hous. [L. casa; Heb. to put on, to cover.] One of the estates of a kingdom assembled in parliament or legislature; a body of men united in their legislative capacity, and holding their place by right or by election.

Thus we say, the *house* of lords or peers of Great Britain; the *house* of commons; the *house* of representatives. In most of the United States, the legislatures consist of two *houses*, the senate, and the *house* of representatives or delegates.

Page 48

†**DEMOCRACY**, n. [Gr. People, and to possess, to govern.] Government by the people; a form of government, in which the supreme power is lodged in the hands of the people collectively, or in which the people exercise the powers of legislation. Such was the government of Athens.

†**REPRESENT'ATIVE**, n. In legislative or other business, an agent, deputy or substitute who supplies the place of another or others, being invested with his or their authority. An attorney is the *representative* of his client or employer. A member of the house of commons is the *representative* of his constituents and of the nation. In matters concerning his constituents only, he is supposed to be bound by their instructions, but in the enacting of laws for the nation, he is supposed not to be bound by their instructions, as he acts for the whole nation.

‡**BANCROFT**; Probably a reference to George Bancroft and his ten volume *History of the United States, From the Discovery of the Continent.* See page 178 for another reference to Bancroft.

Page 49

†**AMPHIC'TYONS**, n. In Grecian history, an assembly or council of deputies from the different states of Greece, supposed to be so called from Amphictyon, the son of Deucalion, but this opinion is probably a fable. Ten or twelve states were represented in this assembly, which sat at Thermophlae, but ordinarily at Delphi. Each city sent two deputies, one called Hieromnemon and the other Pylagoras. The former inspected the sacrifices and ceremonies of religion; the latter, had the charge of deciding causes and differences between private persons. The former was elected by lot; the latter by a plurality of voices. They had an equal right to deliberate and vote in all matters relating to the common interests of Greece.

Page 50

†**CAVALIER**, n. The appellation of the party of **King Charles I**. 1. A horseman, especially an armed horseman; a knight. 2. A gay, sprightly, military man.

‡**KING CHARLES I BEHEADED**; "I cannot attempt to describe to you all the troubles of this reign; the history of this rebellion takes up whole volumes. The Parliament took up arms against the King, and there were many battles between the king's army and theirs. It is dreadful to think of the miseries and slaughter which filled the kingdom, and to reflect, that these were all among fellow-countrymen, who ought to live like friends and brothers, instead of quarreling and killing one another.

"During these wars, **Oliver Cromwell** came forward as an officer in the parliamentary army...King Charles fled...[and] put himself under the protection of the Scotch army, where he was in hopes that he should find friends. He was, however, deceived. The Parliament offered a large sum of money to the Scots, and they gave up their king. The Scotch army returned home loaded with the riches which they had earned by this treacherous and disgraceful action...Many of his subjects who saw him could not help grieving to perceive his altered appearance: he looked pale and sickly; his hair had become grey with sorrow; he had suffered his beard to grow, and his apparel showed all the marks of poverty and distress...

He was soon brought to trial: and when he was produced before the judges, he sat down with all the dignity of a king, without moving his hat, or showing by any such sign that he acknowledged their power to try him. The charge against him was then read, and he was accused of being the cause of all the bloodshed since the beginning of the rebellion...He was four times brought before this assembly of the Commons...and on the fourth day they accordingly pronounced sentence against him...He was allowed three days to prepare for execution...

"The scaffold was...covered with black, and upon it were the block and the axe, and two executioners in masks...The king then came forth, attended by his faithful friend and servant, Bishop Juxon.

"Whilst he was preparing himself for the block, the good bishop said to him, 'There is, Sir, but one stage more, which, though turbulent and troublesome, is yet a very short one...' 'I go,' replied the king, 'from a corruptible to an incorruptible crown, where no disturbance can have place...' Then the king laid his neck on the block, and one of the executioners severed his head from his body at one blow: and the other, holding it up, exclaimed, 'This is the head of a traitor!'" (Source: Bishop Davys, *History of England*)

Page 51

†**COMMONWEALTH**, n. An established form of government, or civil polity; or more generally, a state; a body politic, consisting of a certain portion of men united by compact or tacit agreement, under one form of government and system of laws. This term is applied to the government of Great Britain, which is of a mixed character, and to other governments which are considered as free or popular, but rarely or improperly, to an absolute government. A commonwealth is properly a free state; a popular or representative government; a republic; as the *commonwealth* of Massachusetts. The word signifies strictly, the common good or happiness; and hence, the form of government supposed best to secure the public good.

†**VICIS'SITUDE**, n. [L. vicissitudo; from vicis, a turn.] 1. Regular change or succession of one thing to another; as the *vicissitudes* of day and night, and of winter and summer; the *vicissitudes* of the seasons. 2. Change; revolution; as in human affairs. We are exposed to continual *vicissitudes* of fortune.

Page 52

†**SPECIE**, n. spe'shy. Coin; copper, silver or gold coined and used as a circulating medium of commerce.

†**QUINT'AL**, n. [l. centum, a hundred.] A hundred pounds in weight; or a weight of that number of pounds; sometimes written and pronounced 'kentle'.

Page 53

†**TANK'ARD**, n. A large vessel for liquors, or a drinking vessel, with a cover.

†**BULL'ION**, n. Uncoined gold or silver in the mass. The precious metals are called bullion, when smelted and not perfectly refined, or when refined, but in bars, ingots, or in any form uncoined, as in plate.

†**SMALL'CLOTHES**; Breeches.

Page 55

†**PORTION [DOWERY]**, n. [Gr., a gift; to give. L.] The property which a woman brings to her husband in marriage.

Page 58

†**STEEPLE-HOUSE**, n. A church.

Page 59

‡**MARY DYER**; "Mary Dyer of Rhode Island, in the words of George Bishop, the old Quaker chronicler, written after her death, was 'a Comely Grave Woman, and of a goodly Personage, and one of a good Report, having a Husband of an Estate, fearing the Lord, and a Mother of Children.' **Governor Winthrop** of Massachusetts, a less friendly writer, refers to her, in 1638, as 'the wife of one William Dyer, a milliner in the New Exchange, a very proper and fair woman, and both of them notoriously infected with Mrs. Hutchinson's errors, and very censorious and troublesome, (she being of a very proud spirit, and much addicted to revelations).'" (Source: Horatio Rogers, *Mary Dyer of Rhode Island, the Quaker Martyr That Was Hanged on Boston Common, June 1, 1660*)

Page 60

‡**CHARLES THE SECOND**; "There never were such profligate times in England as under Charles II. Whenever you see his portrait, with his swarthy, ill-looking face and great nose, you may fancy him in his Court at Whitehall, surrounded by some of the very worst vagabonds in the kingdom (though they were lords and ladies), drinking, gambling, indulging in vicious conversation, and committing every kind of profligate excess. It has been a fashion to call Charles the Second 'The Merry Monarch.'" (Source: Charles Dickens, *A Child's History of England*)

‡**QUAKER PERSECUTION**; "The next First-day I went to Tickhill, where the Friends of that side gathered together, and a mighty brokenness by the power of God there was among the people. I went out of the meeting, being moved of God to go to the steeple-house. When I came there, I found the priest and most of the chief people of the parish together in the chancel. I went up to them, and began to speak; but they immediately fell upon me; the clerk up with his Bible, as I was speaking, and' struck me on the face with it, so that my face gushed out with blood; and I bled exceedingly in the steeple-house.' The people cried, ' Let us have him out of the church.' When they had got me out they beat me exceedingly, threw me down, and threw me over a hedge. They afterwards drug me through a house into the street, stoning and beating me as they dragged me along; so that I was all over besmeared with blood and dirt." (Source: **George Fox**, *A Journal*)

Page 62

†**AM'ITY**, n. [L. amo, amicitia.] Friendship, in a general sense, between individuals, societies or nations; harmony; good understanding; as, our nation is in *amity* with all the world; a treaty of *amity* and commerce.

‡**UNCAS**; "Uncas, the Mohegan sachem, was originally a Pequot, and one of the twenty-six war captains of that famous but ill-fated nation. Setting up for himself at the head of the Thames River, near the present city of Norwich, he was politic enough to court the favor of the English, and in 1637 joined with them in their war upon the Pequots. In the pursuit that followed the Fort Mystic fight his men captured a Pequot chief of distinction. Cutting off the captive's head, Uncas placed it in a conspicuous spot near the harbor, where it remained many years. This circumstance gave to Guilford harbor the well-known name of 'Sachem's Head.'" (Source: Francis S. Drake, *Indian History for Young Folks*)

‡**SASSACUS**; "Of the Indian tribes of New England the Pequots were the most formidable. All the other tribes were afraid of them. They were settled near the Thames

River in Connecticut, and could muster seven hundred warriors. In his prosperous days, Sassacus, their sachem, had no less than twenty-six sachems under him, and reigned supreme from Narraganset Bay to the Hudson River, and over Long Island. Seeing the English settlements multiplying around him, and fearing that sooner or later the English would be in possession of the hunting grounds of his tribe, he resolved to make war upon them...[However, the settlers massacred the Pequots, and] this first great blow inflicted on the Indians struck terror into them and secured a long season of peace...The remainder of the tribe were soon hunted down. A portion of them fled for protection to the Mohawks, who treacherously beheaded Sassacus and five other sachems. 'A nation had disappeared from the family of men.'" (Source: Francis S. Drake, *Indian History for Young Folks*)

†**SA'CHEM**, n. In America, a chief among some of the native Indian tribes.

Page 64

‡**BOSTON ATHENÆUM**; The Athenæum library, "....one of the oldest and most distinguished independent libraries in the United States, was founded in 1807 by members of the Anthology Society, a group of fourteen Boston gentlemen who had joined together in 1805 to edit *The Monthly Anthology* and *Boston Review*. Their purpose was to form 'an establishment similar to that of the Athenæum and Lyceum of Liverpool in Great Britain; combining the advantages of a public library [and] containing the great works of learning and science in all languages.'" (Source: *http://www.bostonathenaeum.org*)

Page 66

†**ERUDI'TION**, n. Learning; knowledge gained by study, or from books and instruction; particularly, learning in literature, as distinct from the sciences, as in history, antiquity and languages.

Page 68

†**BUFF[-COAT]**, n. A military coat made of buffskin or similar leather.

BUFFSKIN; n. [contracted from buffalo, or buffskin] A sort of leather, prepared from the skin of the buffalo, dressed with oil, like shammy. It is used for making bandoliers, belts, pouches, gloves and other articles. The skins of oxen, elks and other animals, dressed in like manner, are also called buffs.

†**CORSELET**, n. A little cuirass, or an armor to cover the body for protection, worn formerly by pike-men.

Page 70

‡**LIFE OF JOHN ELIOT**; Referring to *Life of John Eliot, the Apostle to the Indians*, by Convers Francis. See Appendix I on pages 96-100 for an excerpt from this work.

Page 72

‡**KING PHILIP**; "The Pokanoket chief, from his ambitious and haughty spirit, was called King Philip. His Indian name was Pometacom. His pride was shown in his dress, which was rich and gaudy...Tradition says that Philip was averse to the **war**, and that, on hearing that blood had been shed, he wept at the news. However this may be, there can be no doubt of his desire to rid his country of the white intruders, and at the close of the year 1674 he began his preparations in good earnest...[After a year of **raids and skirmishes**,] King Philip, the great and dreaded foe of the white man, was shot by an Indian of **[Benjamin] Church**'s party, whose

brother Philip had killed for counseling submission to the English. In accordance with the barbarous usage of that day, the dead sachem was beheaded and quartered. His head was set upon a gibbet at Plymouth, where it was to be seen for twenty years." (Source: Francis S. Drake, *Indian History for Young Folks*)

‡**BENJAMIN CHURCH**; "Captain Benjamin Church was the most skillful and successful Indian fighter of that day. He was as sagacious and resolute as he was physically powerful and active, and he was greatly feared and respected by the Indians." (Source: Francis S. Drake, *Indian History for Young Folks*)

Page 73

†**REPI'NING**, n. The act of fretting or feeling discontent or of murmuring.

Page 76

†**BIG'OTED**, a. Obstinately and blindly attached to some creed, opinion, practice or ritual; unreasonably devoted to a system or party, and illiberal towards the opinions of others.

†**DESPOTIC**, a. Absolute in power; independent of control from men, constitution or laws; arbitrary in the exercise of power; as a *despotic* prince.

‡**CHARTERS TAKEN AWAY**; "There was too much liberty in America to suit the King of England. The people of Massachusetts, under the charter given them by the grandfather of **Charles II**, were making their own laws and governing themselves, and Charles II determined to take it from them...but Death stepped suddenly in, putting an end to a worthless life. His brother, the Duke of York, became **King James II**...James had determined to carry out his brother's plan...It was the beginning of absolute government in Massachusetts... [James appointed **Sir Edmund Andros** governor of Massachusetts, who] ruled as he pleased, giving to his friends not only fat offices, but the farms which people had bought and paid for. Having established his authority in Massachusetts, he went to Connecticut, to take away the charter which **Governor Winslow** had obtained from Charles II...New England, for the time being, was under his heel." (Source: Charles Carleton Coffin, *Old Times in the Colonies*)

Page 77

‡**WILLIAM THE THIRD**; "On the 29th of May a vessel sailed into the harbor, bringing joyful news. William, Prince of Orange, was King of England, and there was an end forever of absolute rule in England. In commemoration of the event the people of Boston sat down to a grand dinner in the Town House, providing an abundance of wine, everybody eating and drinking till the sexton rung the bell at nine o'clock in the evening, when they made their way home, rejoicing over the downfall of **King James**, **Andros**, and all their minions." (Source: Charles Carleton Coffin, *Old Times in the Colonies*)

Page 81

†**GUBERNATO'RIAL**, a. [L. gubernator.] Pertaining to government, or to a governor.

Page 82

†**PER'IWIG**, n. A wig; a kind of close cap formed by an intertexture of false hair, worn by men for ornament or to conceal baldness. Periwigs were in fashion in the days of Addison.

†**BEDIZ'EN**, v.t. bediz'n. [be and dizen.] To adorn; to deck; a low word.

†**ADZ**, n. An iron instrument with an arching edge, across the line of the handle, and ground from a base on its inside to the outer edge; used for chipping a horizontal surface of timber.

Page 83

†**KNEE**, n. nee. [L. genu.] In ship-building, a piece of timber somewhat in the shape of the human knee when bent, having two branches or arms, and used to connect the beams of a ship with her sides or timbers.

Page 88

†**GRANDEE'**, n. A nobleman; a man of elevated rank or station. In Spain, a nobleman of the first rank, who has the king's leave to be covered in his presence.

Page 89

‡**KING MIDAS**; "In Greek mythology, king of Phrygia, whose request that whatsoever he touched should turn to gold was granted by the god Dionysus (Bacchus). In this way even his food became gold, and it was not until he had bathed in the Pactolus that the fatal gift was transferred to the river." (Source: *Winston's Cumulative Loose-leaf Encyclopedia: A Comprehensive Reference Work* edited by Thomas Edward Finegan)

Page 92

†**IN'TERCOURSE**, n. [L. intercursus, intercurro; inter and curro, to run.] Literally, a running or passing between. Hence, 1. Communication; commerce; connection by reciprocal dealings between persons or nations, either in common affairs and civilities, in trade, or correspondence by letters. We have an *intercourse* with neighbors and friends in mutual visits and in social concerns; nations and individuals have *intercourse* with foreign nations or individuals by an interchange of commodities, by purchase and sale, by treaties, contracts, &c. 2. Silent communication or exchange.

Page 96

†**ASSID'UOUS**, a. [L. assiduus, from assideo, to sit close, ad and sedeo; Eng. to sit.] Performed with constant diligence or attention; as *assiduous* labor.

†**CONVERSANT**, a. Acquainted by familiar use or study. We correct our style, and improve our taste, by being *conversant* with the best classical writers. In the foregoing applications, this word is most generally followed by 'with', according to present usage. 'In' was formerly used; and both 'in' and 'among' may be used.

†**AFFIN'ITY**, n. [L. affinitas, from affinis, adjacent, related by marriage; ad and finis, end.] Agreement; relation; conformity; resemblance; connection; as, the *affinity* of sounds, of colors, or of languages.

†**SAGAC'ITY**, n. [L. sagacitas.] Quickness or acuteness of discernment or penetration; readiness of apprehension; the faculty of readily discerning and distinguishing ideas, and of separating truth from falsehood.

Page 97

†**INTEL'LIGIBLE**, a. [L. intelligibilis.] That may be understood or comprehended;

as an intelligible account. The rules of human duty are *intelligible* to minds of the smallest capacity.

†**FACIL'ITY**, n. [L. facilitas, from facilis, easy.] Ease of performance; readiness proceeding from skill or use; dexterity. Practice gives a wonderful *facility* in executing works of art.

†**LAMENT', v.i. [L. lamentor.]** 1. To mourn; to grieve; to weep or wail; to express sorrow. 2. To regret deeply; to feel sorrow.

Page 98

‡**EZEKIEL 37:9, 10**; "Then said he to me, Prophesy to the wind, prophesy, son of man, and say to the wind, Thus saith the Lord GOD; Come from the four winds, O breath, and breathe upon these slain, that they may live. So I prophesied as he commanded me, and the breath came into them, and they lived, and stood up upon their feet, an exceeding great army." (Source: Daniel Webster's *Bible*)

†**CONSTRUE**, v.t. [L.] To interpret; to explain; to show or to understand the meaning.

†**PROV'IDENCE**, n. [L. providentia.] 1. Foresight; timely care; particularly, active foresight, or foresight accompanied with the procurement of what is necessary for future use, or with suitable preparation. How many of the troubles and perplexities of life proceed from want of *providence*! 2. In theology, the care and superintendence which God exercises over his creatures. He that acknowledges a creation and denies a *providence*, involves himself in a palpable contradiction; for the same power which caused a thing to exist is necessary to continue its existence. Some persons admit a general providence, but deny a particular providence, not considering that a general providence consists of particulars. A belief in divine *providence,* is a source of great consolation to good men. By divine *providence* is often understood God himself.

†**COUNTENANCE**, n. [L., to hold.] Support; aid; patronage; encouragement; favor in promoting and maintaining a person or cause.

Page 99

†**ZEAL**, n. [Gr., L.] Passionate ardor in the pursuit of any thing. In general, zeal is an eagerness of desire to accomplish or obtain some object, and it may be manifested either in favor of any person or thing, or in opposition to it, and in a good or bad cause.

†**INTERCE'DE**, v.i. [L. intercedo; inter and cedo; literally, to move or pass between.] To mediate; to interpose; to make intercession; to act between parties with a view to reconcile those who differ or contend; usually followed by 'with'.

Page 103

†**AN'THRACITE**, n. [Gr. a burning coal; infra.] Slaty glance-coal, or columnar glance coal; that species of coal which has a shining luster, approaching to metallic, and which burns without smoke, and with intense heat. It consists essentially of carbon.

Page 105

†**VULGAR** , a. Common; used by all classes of people; as the *vulgar* version of the scriptures.

‡**PETER THE GREAT** "If I were called upon to name the man who, since Charlemagne, has rendered the greatest services to his country, I should select Peter the Great. I do not say that he is one of the most interesting characters that has shone in the noble constellations of illustrious benefactors whom Europe has produced. Far otherwise: his career is not so interesting to us as that of Hildebrand, or **Elizabeth**, or **Cromwell**, or Richelieu, or Gustavus Adolphus, or **William III**, or Louis XIV, or Frederic II, or others I might mention. I have simply to show an enlightened barbarian toiling for civilization, a sort of Hercules cleansing Augean stables and killing Nemean lions; a man whose labors were prodigious; a very extraordinary man, stained by crimes and cruelties, yet laboring, with a sort of inspired enthusiasm, to raise his country from an abyss of ignorance and brutality. It would be difficult to find a more hard-hearted despot, and yet a more patriotic sovereign. To me he looms up, even more than Richelieu, as an instrument of Divine Providence. His character appears in a double light,–as benefactor and as tyrant, in order to carry out ends which he deemed useful to his country, and which, we are constrained to admit, did wonderfully contribute to its elevation and political importance." (Source: John Lord, LL.D., *Beacon Lights of History*, Volume VIII)

Page 108

‡**WITCHCRAFT DELUSION**; "...I will collect, as far as I am able, the several instances of what was called Witchcraft, from the beginning of the country.

"It is natural to suppose that the country, at the first entrance of the Europeans into it, afforded the most suitable scene, especially as a notion prevailed that the savages all worshipped the Devil; but I find no mention of witchcraft for the first twelve or fifteen years. About the year 1645, several people in Springfield, upon Connecticut River, were suspected of witchcraft, and a greater number were supposed to be bewitched; among the rest two of the minister's children. Great pains were taken to prove the facts upon the suspected persons; and about the year 1650, a poor wretch, Mary Oliver, no doubt weary of her life, after long examination, was brought to confession. It does not appear that she was executed.

"Whilst this inquiry was making, Margaret Jones was executed at Charlestown. Mention is made by Mr. Hale, of a woman at Dorchester, and another at Cambridge about the same time, all denying what they were charged with, at their death; and soon after Mrs. Hibbins the magistrate's widow, was executed at Boston...**Goffe, the Regicide**, says in his diary, January 20, 1662, that three witches were condemned at Hartford...

"Another ventriloqua, Elizabeth Knap, at Groton, in 1671, much as Ann Cole had done at Hartford, alarmed the people there...In 1673, Eunice Cole, of Hampton, was tried, and the jury found her not legally guilty; but that there were strong grounds to suspect her of familiarity with the Devil.

"In 1679, the house of William Morse, of Newbury, was troubled with throwing bricks, stones and sticks, and playing so many pranks that he that believes the story told by Glanvil of the devils at Tedworth cannot avoid giving credit to this. It is worth observing that none of the family, except one boy, were afflicted...

"In 1683, the demons removed to Connecticut River again, where the house of one Desborough was molested, and stones, earth, &c. thrown at him, not only through the windows, but doors, by an invisible band; and a fire, kindled nobody knew how, burnt up no small part of his estate. It seems one of Desborough's neighbors had a quarrel with him about a chest of clothes which Desborough detained; and, as soon as they were restored, the troubles ceased. All was charged upon the demons, and nobody, from anything which now appears, suspected the honest neighbor.

"In 1681, the house of George Walton, a Quaker, at Portsmouth, in New Hampshire, was attacked in much the same manner. Walton had contention with a woman about a tract of land, and she was supposed to have done the mischief but by witchcraft...

"In 1685, a large and circumstantial account of all or most of these instances was published, and anybody who doubted the truth of them would have been pronounced a Sadducee.

"In 1688 begun a more alarming instance than any which preceded it. Four of the children of John Goodwin, a grave man and good liver at the north part of Boston, were generally believed to be bewitched. I have often heard those who were then upon the stage, speak of the great consternation it occasioned. The children were all remarkable for an ingenuity of temper, had been religiously educated, and were supposed to be incapable of imposture or fraud...

"One thing was remarkable, and ought to have been taken more notice of, that all their complaints were in the day time, and that they slept comfortably all night. They were sometimes deaf, then dumb, then blind, and sometimes all these together. Their tongues would be drawn down their throats, then pulled out upon their chins. Their jaws, necks, shoulders, elbows, and all their joints would appear to be dislocated, and they would make the most piteous outcries of being cut with knives and beat; and plain marks of wounds might afterwards be discovered. The ministers of Boston and Charlestown kept a day of fasting and prayer at the troubled house; and after that the youngest child made no more complaints. But the magistrates unfortunately interposed; and the old woman was apprehended, examined, committed and brought to trial, and seems neither to have owned nor denied her guilt, being either really a distracted person, or endeavoring to appear such; and, before sentence of death was passed, the opinion of physicians was taken; but they returned that she was *compos mentis*, and she was executed, declaring at her death the children should not, or perhaps it might be, would not be relieved by her death, and that others besides her had a hand in their afflictions...

"The eldest is after this the principal subject; and was taken into a minister's family, where for some days she behaved orderly, but after that suddenly fell into her fits. The relation chiefly consists of their being violently beaten by specters; put into red hot ovens, and their sweating and panting; having cold water thrown upon them, and then shivering; being roasted upon invisible spits; having their heads nailed to the floor, so as that they could hardly be pulled away; their joints first stiff and then limber; pins stuck into their flesh; choked until they were black in the face; having the witches invisible chain upon them, dancing with a chair, like one riding on horseback; being able to read bad books, and blind if they looked into a good one; being drunk without anything to intoxicate.

"There is nothing in all this but what may be accounted for from craft and fraud, which children of that age are very capable of; or from agility of body, in which these children are exceeded by common tumblers much younger...

"At Salem was the next scene, and more tragical by far than any which had preceded...Many of the ministers of the country, who were much consulted in this affair, had a confirmed opinion of a very familiar intercourse between the visible and invisible worlds. This, together with the books which had been brought into the country not long before, containing relations of the like things in England, rendered the minds of the people in general susceptible of credit to every the like story related here. The works of Perkins and other non-conformist divines were in the hands of many, and there is no doubt that Goodwin's children had read or heard the stories in Glanvil, having very exactly imitated them...

"**Sir William Phips**, the Governor just arrived, seems to have given in to the prevailing opinion. He was much under the direction of the spiritual fathers of the country...Even to this day, the country seems rather to be divided in opinion whether it was the accused or the afflicted who were under some preternatural or diabolical possession, than whether the afflicted were under bodily distempers, or altogether guilty of fraud and imposture...In February, 1691, a daughter and a niece of Mr. Parris, the minister of Salem village, girls of ten or eleven years of age, and one or two more girls in the neighborhood, made the same sort of complaints as Goodwin's children had done two or three four years before. The physicians, having no other way of accounting for the disorder, pronounced them bewitched

"[Many] unhappy people were not only...brought to confession, but also obliged to swear to the truth of it...The prison at Salem was so full that some were obliged to be removed, and many were in other prisons reserved for trial...Some of the persons were publicly named. Dudley Bradstreet, a justice of the peace, who had been appointed one of President Dudley's council, thought it necessary to abscond; so did his brother John Bradstreet, sons of the late **Governor Bradstreet**. Calef says it was intimated that Sir William Phips's lady was accused...

"The juries changed sooner than the judges. The opinion which the latter had of their own superior understanding and judgment probably made them more backward in owning or discovering their errors...One of the ministers, who in the time of it approved of the court's proceeding, remarked in his diary soon after that many were of opinion innocent blood had been shed. The afflicted were never brought to trial for their imposture. Many of them are said to have proved profligate, abandoned people, and others to have passed the remainder of their lives in a state of obscurity and contempt." (Source: **Gov. Thomas Hutchinson**, *The Witchcraft Delusion of 1692*)

Page 109

‡**GEORGE BURROUGHS**; "At the Superior Court...there was one Margaret Jacobs, who had more courage than the rest. She had been brought not only to accuse herself, but Mr. Burroughs, the minister, and even her own grandfather. Before their execution, she was struck with horror, and begged forgiveness of Burroughs, who readily forgave her, and prayed with her, and for her." (Source: **Gov. Thomas Hutchinson**, *The Witchcraft Delusion of 1692*)

Page 111

COLLECTOR [of BOSTON], n. An officer appointed and commissioned to collect and receive customs, duties,

‡**SPANIARDS**; Referring to the history of **Christopher Columbus** and Spanish gold. **Francisco Roldan**, "a Spaniard who had once been a servant of the Admiral's [Christopher Columbus], and who had been raised by him to the office of judge in the island [Hispaniola]–an able creature, but, like too many recipients of Christopher's favour, a treacherous rascal at bottom. As soon as the Admiral's back was turned Roldan had begun to make mischief, stirring up the discontent that was never far below the surface of life in the colony, and getting together a large band of rebellious ruffians." (Source: Filson Young, *Christopher Columbus*)

For the next couple of years, Roldan led a rebellion against Columbus, who finally negotiated terms of conciliation humiliating to himself. Meanwhile, charges of tyranny and misrule against Columbus had reached King Ferdinand and Queen Isabella of Spain, who in 1500 sent **Francis de Bovadilla**, "a poor knight of the order of Calatrava", to investigate. However, as soon as Bovadilla arrived in Hispaniola, he "immediately took possession of the admirals palace, and appropriated every thing he found there to his own use as if it had fallen to him by inheritance. He gathered together all whom he could find who had been in rebellion [including Roldan], and many others who hated the admiral and his brothers, and immediately declared himself governor of the colony." (Source: Robert Kerr, *A General History and Collection of Voyages and Travels*, Vol. III)

Bovadilla sent Columbus back to Spain in chains, where upon arrival, he was vindicated. Another investigator named Ovando was sent from Spain to Hispaniola, this time to investigate Bovadilla. Ovando "found the island in a shocking state, the Spanish population having to a man devoted itself to idleness, profligacy, and slave-driving. The only thing that had prospered was the gold mining; for owing to the licence that Bobadilla had given to the Spaniards to employ native labor to an unlimited extent there had been an immense amount of gold taken from the mines." Bovadilla and Rodin were arrested and, along with a massive amount of gold, were put on board one of 18 ships that were headed back to Spain. "But the large home-going fleet" did not survive. A hurricane, "which was probably from the northeast, struck them just as they lost the lee of the island, and many of them, including the ships with the treasure of gold and the caravels bearing Roldan, Bobadilla, and Guarionex, all went down at once and were never seen or heard of again." (Source: Filson Young, *Christopher Columbus*.)

Page 114

†**GIRD'LE**, n. A band or belt; something drawn round the waist of a person, and tied or buckled; as a girdle of fine lines; a leathern girdle.

Page 115

†**FER'ULE**, n. [L. ferula, from ferio, to strike, or from the use of stalks of the Ferula.] A little wooden pallet or slice, used to punish children in school, by striking them on the palm of the hand.

†**CON**, v.t. [to know, to be able, to be skillful or wise; and to bear or bring forth, Gr. To try, to attempt, to prove, L., whence cunning, skillful, experienced, or skill, experience; coincides in sense with to begin, to try to attempt. G. To know; to be able. The primary sense is, to strain or stretch, which gives the sense of strength, power, as in can, and of holding, containing, comprehending, as contain, from contineo, teneo, Gr., L. To beget or to bring forth. In the sense of know, con signifies to hold or to reach.] To make ones self master of; to fix in the mend or commit to memory; as, to *con* a lesson.

†**ASAFETIDA**, n. [Asa, gum, and L. fatidus, fetid.] Asafetida, a fetid gum-resin, from the East Indies. It is the concrete juice of a large unbelliferous plant, much used in Medicine, as an antispasmodic.

Page 116

†**UNC'TION**, n. [L. unctio, from ungo, to anoint.] Divine or sanctifying grace.

‡**VIRGIL** Publius Vergilius Maro, "was born at Andes near Mantua, in the year 70 B.C. His life was uneventful, though he lived in stirring times, and he passed by far the greater part of it in reading his books and writing his poems, undisturbed by the fierce civil strife which continued to rage throughout the Roman Empire, until Octavian, who afterwards became the Emperor Augustus, defeated Antony at the battle of Actium. Though his father was a man of humble origin, Virgil received an

excellent education, first at Cremona and Milan, and afterwards at Rome. He was intimate with all the distinguished men of his time, and a personal friend of the Emperor. After the publication of his second work, the *Georgics*, he was recognized as being the greatest poet of his age, and the most striking figure in the brilliant circle of literary men, which was centred at the Court. He died at Brindisi in the spring of 19 B.C. whilst returning from a journey to Greece, leaving his greatest work, the *Aeneid*, written but unrevised. It was published by his executors, and immediately took its place as the great national Epic of the Roman people. Virgil seems to have been a man of simple, pure, and lovable character, and the references to him in the works of Horace clearly show the affection with which he was regarded by his friends." (Source: Introduction from *The Aeneid of Virgil*, Everyman's Library, translated by E. Fairfax Taylor, edited by Ernest Rhys.)

Page 117

†**CAMBRIC**, n. A species of fine white linen, made of flax, said to be named from Cambray in Flanders, where it was first manufactured.

†**LAP'STONE**, n. A stone on which shoemakers beat leather, and held on the knees.

†**MALEFAC'TOR**, n. [supra.] One who commits a crime; one guilty of violating the laws, in such a manner as to subject him to public prosecution and punishment, particularly to capital punishment; a criminal.

Page 120

†**AC'CIDENCE**, n. A small book containing the rudiments of grammar.

†**PEDANT'IC**, a. Ostentatious of learning; vainly displaying or making a show of knowledge; applied to persons or things; as a *pedantic* writer or scholar; a *pedantic* description or expression.

Page 122

†**QUART'O**, n. [L. quartus.] A book of the size of the fourth of a sheet; a size made by twice folding a sheet, which then makes four leaves.

†**DUODECIMO**, n. A book in which a sheet is folded into twelve leaves.

‡**BABEL**; "And the whole earth was of one language, and of one speech. And it came to pass as they journeyed from the east, that they found a plain in the land of Shinar, and they dwelt there. And they said one to another, come, let us make brick, and burn them thoroughly. And they had brick for stone, and slime [tar] had they for mortar. And they said, come, let us build us a city, and a tower, whose top may reach to heaven; and let us make us a name, lest we should be scattered abroad upon the face of the whole earth. And the LORD came down to see the city and the tower, which the children of men were building. And the LORD said, Behold, the people is one, and they have all one language; and this they begin to do: and now nothing will be restrained from them, which they have imagined to do. Come, let us go down, and there confound their language, that they may not understand one another's speech. So the LORD scattered them abroad from thence upon the face of all the earth: and they left off to build the city. Therefore is the name of it called Babel, because the LORD there confounded the language of all the earth: and from thence did the LORD scatter them abroad upon the face of all the earth." (Source: Daniel Webster's *Bible,* **Gen. 11:1-9**)

Page 123

†**ME'AGER**, a. [L. macer; Gr. small; allied to Eng. meek.] Thin; lean; destitute of flesh

or having little flesh; applied to animals.

Page 127

‡**TOWN HOUSE**; "The first Town House was erected between 1657-59, at the head of State Street, of wood, where the Old State House now stands...This building was consumed in the fire of 1711; another, built of brick in 1712, was burnt in 1747, with the early books, records, and valuable papers. In 1748 the Town House was rebuilt. **Faneuil Hall** was also used as a Town House for nearly eighty years, and the first city government was organized there. In 1830 the city government removed to the Old State House, which was, on September 17, dedicated as the City Hall." (Source: Samuel Adams Drake, *Old Landmarks and Historic Personages of Boston*)

Page 128

‡**GOVERNOR [JOSEPH] DUDLEY**; "In 1707, at the death of Samuel Willard, President of Harvard College, if learning alone had been a sufficient qualification, **Cotton Mather** would have been selected to fill the vacancy; and he was so confident of receiving the appointment, that he observed days of fasting, after his usual manner, to solicit the divine direction. But Governor Dudley prevailed on Judge Leverett, who is one of his Council, and in every respect fitted for the trust, to accept the office, which he filled with usefulness and honor for many years. This appointment was a signal to the Mathers, that their influence was at an end, and they made no secret of their displeasure. While President Leverett was in the chair, they seldom, if ever, attended the meetings of the Overseers. Cotton Mather was not honored with a place in the Corporation, while he was compelled to see Doctor Coleman and Mr. Brattle, men with whom he was not on friendly terms, members of that board, and holding the concerns of the institution in their own control...A passage found in Cotton Mather's Diary, dated June 16th, 1702, shows what kind of language he thought himself authorized to hold to the governor, and how much he was exasperated to find his counsels disregarded...the alienation, combined with other causes, created so much discontent in Cotton Mather, that, in 1707, he addressed a letter to Governor Dudley, which seems intended for no other purpose, than to express his own displeasure." (Source: Jared Sparks, *The Library of American Biography*, Vol. 6)

"The Mather interest, which had been growing cold toward the governor and had been secretly against him, now became violently and openly hostile...they now accused Dudley of procuring by intimidation and corrupt means..." The charges were investigated in England and dismissed as "frivolous". The Mathers, "smarting under the sense of defeat, addressed two violent letters to Dudley....Increase Mather accused him of murdering Leisler, of bribery, of planning to ruin the colony, of falseness to the college...[Cotton Mather] accuses him of covetousness and bribery, of improper use of commissions, of intimidation of the Council and the House, and of intentionally sparing Port Royal at the time of the Church expedition in order to enjoy the illegal trade. 'The whole affair of those grateful merchants,' he declares, 'will by degrees be brought to light.' Dudley's reply was in the form of a joint letter which must have cut the Mathers to the quick. Little attempt was made to answer charges so wild and vague; but the governor gravely reproved both father and son, expressed astonishment that they should forget their station, and hoped that soon they would come to their senses." (Source: Everett Kimball, *The Public Life of Joseph Dudley: A Study of the Colonial Policy of the Stuarts in New England*)

‡**COLONEL [SAMUEL] SHUTE**; "Far...reaching in the principals involved and in its methods was the struggle over official salaries in Massachusetts. The battle began with the appointment of Colonel Shute as Governor in 1716. The conclusion of peace with France had left a large number of unemployed soldiers, with claims on the Crown, and a colonial governorship was an easy and obvious form of recog-

nition. Such were Hunter in New York and Spotswood in Virginia. Shute may not have had the exceptional tact and conciliatory temper of Hunter, nor the strenuous energy and public spirit of Spotswood. But he appears to have been a painstaking, conscientious, and clear-headed official. Unfortunately his lot was cast among a community which could be understood and controlled only by a man of exceptional perception, experience, and strength of will. Throughout the eighteenth century the representative of royalty was to the politicians of New England a man to be suspected, thwarted, and outwitted, and we shall find over and over again men who in other colonies would have had creditable careers failing when brought face to face with those persistent and often unscrupulous masters of political strategy who guided the councils of Massachusetts." (Source: John Andrew Doyle, *English Colonies in America*)

‡**LIEUTENANT-GOVERNOR [WILLIAM] DUMMER**; "Dummer's War from 1722 to 1725 marked the climax in **Indian warfare** in Maine. Before this, aggressors [preyed] upon defenseless and weak hamlets; now the Indians themselves were hunted. The old town at Old Town and the new town and Eddington Bend were burned, Norridgewock was taken by surprise with great slaughter, and its priest, Father Rale, was killed. A little band of English soldiers, in Lovewell's fight at Fryeburg, May, 1725, surrounded and outnumbered, with everything against them, held out in an all-day fight and not only held the ground against a large fighting band, but practically broke it up. After this, Indian warfare in Maine was sporadic, and after the French were defeated at Quebec, it ceased altogether. When the French joined the colonists in the Revolution, the Maine Indians became entirely friendly and never since have they disturbed the peace of their white neighbors." (Source: Henry Ernest Dunnack, *The Maine Book*)

Page 132

‡**GALEN AND HIPPOCRATES**; "The greatest name in medical science in ancient or in modern times, the man who did the most to advance it, the greatest medical genius of whom we have any early record, was **Hippocrates**, born on the island of Cos, 460 B.C., of the great Aesculapian family. He received his instruction from his father. We know scarcely more of his life than we do of Homer himself, although he lived in the period of the highest splendor of Athens. Even his writings, like those of Homer, are thought by some to be the work of different men. They were translated into Arabic, and were no slight means of giving an impulse to the Saracenic schools of the Middle Ages in that science in which the Saracens especially excelled. The Hippocratic collection consists of more than sixty works, which were held in the highest estimation by the ancient physicians. Hippocrates introduced a new era in medicine, which before his time had been monopolized by the priests. He carried out a system of severe induction from the observation of facts, and is as truly the creator of the inductive method as Bacon himself. He abhorred theories which could not be established by facts; he was always open to conviction, and candidly confessed his mistakes; he was conscientious in the practice of his profession, and valued the success of his art more than silver and gold...

"Medical science at Rome culminated in **Galen**, as it did at Athens in Hippocrates. Galen was patronized by Marcus Aurelius, and availed himself of all the knowledge of preceding naturalists and physicians. He was born at Pergamos about the year 130 A.D., where he learned, under able masters, anatomy, pathology, and therapeutics. He finished his studies at Alexandria, and came to Rome at the invitation of the Emperor. Like his imperial patron, Galen was one of the brightest ornaments of the heathen world, and one of the most learned and accomplished men of any age. He left five hundred treatises, most of them relating to some branch of medical science, which give him the name of being one of the most voluminous of authors." (Source: John Lord, LL.D., *Beacon Lights of History*, Volume III, *Ancient Achieve-*

ments)

Page 136

‡**BELOVED SON**; "**Cotton Mather** had read of what inoculation might do, but his proposal to introduce it in Boston 'raised an horrid Clamour.' In his son Samuel, afterwards a distinguished minister, he found the brave abettor of his plan; the boy offered himself for experiment. With deep searching of heart the father, like another Abraham, put his beliefs to the test. The boy fell rapidly sick and came so near to death as to fill his father's soul with fear and the town with uproar. But one day his **Bible**, opened at random, bore him the welcome message, 'Go thy way, thy son liveth.' And the promise was fulfilled." (Source: Mark Antony De Wolfe Howe, *Boston, the Place and the People*)

‡**PHYSICIAN'S ADVICE**; "[**Dr. Zabdiel Boylston**'s] custom was to make a couple of incisions in the arms, into which bits of lint dipped in pox-matter were inserted. At the end of twenty-four hours the lint was withdrawn, and the wounds dressed with warm cabbage leaves. On the seventh day the patient sickened and pustules appeared, sometimes few, sometimes hundreds. **Mather** and **Boylston** maintained it was a most wholesome operation, for after it 'feeble, crazy, consumptive people, grew hearty, and got rid of their former maladies.'" (Source: William White, *The Story of a Great Delusion in a Series of Matter-of-fact Chapters*)

‡**HAND GRENADE**; "'[H]is 'kinsman, the minister of Roxbury,' came to [Cotton Mather's] house for inoculation. One night during the patient's illness some unknown ruffian threw into the window of the room where he lay a heavy iron 'grenado' charged with powder and oil of turpentine. By some good chance it did not explode; and on it was found a paper bearing the words, "**Cotton Mather**, you Dog; Dam you; I'll inoculate you with this, with a pox to you.'" (Source: Mark Antony De Wolfe Howe, *Boston, the Place and the People*)

Page 137

‡**PEABODY**; Perhaps referring to *Life of Cotton Mather* by William B. O. Peabody.

‡**ELISHA COOKE**; "[Elisha] Cooke settled in Boston as a physician, and, without relinquishing his profession, became an active politician...Mr. Cooke was a gentleman of good understanding, and had been well educated, had always adhered stiffly to the old charter, and when all the rest of the assistants declined reassuming it, he alone was in favor of it..." (Source: John Langdon Sibley and Clifford Kenyon Shipton, *Biographical Sketches of Graduates of Harvard University in Cambridge, Massachusetts*)"

Page 141

‡**PROVINCE HOUSE**; "The Province House, a three-story brick structure, stood nearly opposite the head of Milk Street, with a handsome lawn in front shaded by stately oaks. The interior was on a scale of princely magnificence; the reception room on the first floor was paneled with rich wood and hung with tapestry. It was the great audience hall of the governors. Twenty massive red freestone steps led to the spacious entrance under the grand portico." (Source: Nathan Gillett Pond, *The Magazine of American History with Notes and Queries*)

†**LIV'ERY**, n. A form of dress by which noblemen and gentlemen distinguish their servants.

‡**IRISH GIRLS**; "Most of the service during the early colonial period was performed by 'redemptioners,' and...literature is full of interesting allusion to the terms of

their contracts. Lechford tells us in his *Notebooks of Elizabeth Evans*, who came from Ireland to serve John Wheelwright, minister, for three years, her wages being three pounds per annum and passage paid, and of Margery Bateman, who, after five years of service in Charlestown, was to receive a she-goat to help her in starting in life. In the *Boston News-Letter* may be found an advertisement in which Robert Galton offers 'a few boy servants indentured for seven years and girls for four years', while Mrs. Johnson's *Captivity* tells of apprenticed servants bound for a term of years who, in 1730, were sold from ships in Boston. As late as August 1, 1817, indeed, Samuel Breck, a Bostonian then living in Philadelphia, wrote with no sense of shame:

> 'I went on board the ship *John* from Amsterdam...and I purchased one German Swiss for Mrs. Ross and two French Swiss for myself...'"

(Source: Mary Caroline Crawford, *Social Life in Old New England*)

‡**NEGRO BABIES**; "I have found Negroes advertised in the same newspaper list with tea, velvet, and candles; and Randolph could report two hundred slaves here in 1676. The Quakers protested vigorously against the slave trade in Rhode Island, yet Newport continued to be the receiving and disbursing center for most of the Negroes brought from Guinea and Madagascar.

"Not only were Negroes of both sexes bought and sold, but Indians also appear to have been leased out as household drudges. In the New England Weekly Journal of March 17, 1729, I find advertised:

> 'An Indian Woman's Time for about 2 Years, who can do all sorts of Household Work.'"

(Source: Mary Caroline Crawford, *Social Life in Old New England*)

"In 1645, the General Court of Massachusetts sent back to Guinea two black men illegally enslaved, and made a law forbidding the sale of slaves, except captives in war, or men sentenced for crime. Even they were set free after several years' service. Still **slavery** always existed in spite of the law; the newspapers once contained advertisements of 'negro-babies to be given away' in Boston! Yet New England never loved slavery; as hard and cruel as the Puritans were, they had some respect for the letter of the New Testament." (Source: Theodore Parker, *Additional Speeches, Addresses, and Occasional Sermons*)

Page 143

‡**PERIWIGS**; "[Samuel] Pepys, who was an amateur in wigs, wonders, naïvely, 'what will be the fashion after the plague is done, as to periwigs, for nobody will dare to buy any hair, for fear of the infection, that it had been cut off the heads of the people dead with the plague.' But the fashion outlived even this blow, and an old writer pointedly says that 'Forty or fourscore pounds a year for periwigs, and ten to a poor chaplain to say grace to him that adores hair, is sufficient demonstration of the weakness of the brains they keep warm.'" (Source: *Harper's New Monthly Magazine*, Vol. XVIII)

†**CAPARISON**, n. A cloth or covering laid over the saddle or furniture of a horse, especially a sumpter horse or horse of state. v.t. To dress pompously; to adorn with rich dress.

Page 144

‡**GOVERNOR [JONATHAN] BELCHER**; "[Belcher] had not a generous nature, but in traits which attract popular good-will he was not wanting. His person and presence were graceful and pleasing. He had a cheerful countenance, a hearty voice,

a demonstrative gesticulation, and an habitually affable address. He was a man of society and of the world. Though foolishly irritable, and prone to small resentments which he pursued without dignity, he was not troubled, like his differently constituted and differently trained predecessor, with pride and obstinacy about points of honor. He loved intrigue and tortuous methods...If greedy in acquisition, he was no miser. He spent his money with an elegant liberality...Great surprise was felt when, at the height of the quarrel with Burnet about a stated salary, it became known that Belcher had embraced the popular pretension." (John Gorham Palfrey and Francis Winthrop Palfrey, *History of New England*)

Page 146

‡**STRONGEST FORTRESS**; "... The French founded and built...the city of **Louisbourg**, at enormous cost, and protected it with fortresses of great strength. The walls of the defenses were formed with bricks brought from France, and they mounted 206 pieces of cannon. The city had nunneries and palaces, gardens, squares, and places of amusement, and was designed to become a great capital, and to perpetuate French dominion and the Catholic faith in America. Twenty-five years of time, and 30 million of *livres* in money were spent in building, arming, and adorning the city, "the Dunkirk of the New World." That such a place existed at so early a period of our history, is a marvel; and the lovers of the wonderful may read the works which contain accounts of its rise and ruin, and be satisfied that 'truth is sometimes stranger than fiction.'" (Lorenzo Sabine, *Biographical Sketches of Loyalists of the American Revolution*)

Page 148

‡**WILLIAM PEPPERELL**; "It was of the first importance to find a commander capable both of keeping up the enthusiasm that had been excited for the enterprise, and of conducting its operations with spirit and good judgment. The choice fell upon William Pepperell, of Kettery...He was so far without qualification for the capture of a fortified place, as that he had never seen a siege. But in this he was no worse off than any other New England officer. He would have to be governed by his good sense, and to devise methods as fast as he might, under the instruction of experience. His courage, discretion, probity, and patriotism were notorious and unquestionable." (John Gorham Palfrey and Francis Winthrop Palfrey, *History of New England*)

Page 149

‡**[MUSKET]-REST**; "The musket rest, which the soldier had to carry in his left hand, was of ash wood, with a half hoop of iron, to rest the musket on, at one end, and an iron pike at the other, to fix it in the ground." (Source: Sir Clements R. Markham, *"The Fighting Veres"*)

†**TOUCH-HOLE**, n. tuch'-hole. [touch and hole.] The vent of a cannon or other species of fire-arms, by which fire is communicated to the powder of the charge. It is now called the vent.

†**GARRETT**, n. attic

Page 150

†**COMMON**, n. A tract of ground, the use of which is not appropriated to an individual, but belongs to the public or to a number. Thus we apply the word to an open ground or space in a highway, reserved for public use.

Page 152

†**CUPOLA**, n. In architecture, a spherical vault on the top of an edifice; a dome, or the round top of a dome.

Page 153

‡**LOUISBOURG HAS SURRENDERED!**; [**Pepperell's**] troops consisted of a motley assemblage of fishermen and farmers, sawyers and loggers, many of whom were taken from [Pepperell's] own vessels, mills, and forests. Before such men, and before others hardly better skilled in war, in the year 1745, Louisbourg fell. The achievement is the most memorable in our Colonial annals." (Lorenzo Sabine, *Biographical Sketches of Loyalists of the American Revolution*)

Page 155

‡**DUKE D'ANVILLE**; "...Fortune had no favors for the unhappy d'Anville. Before he was clear of the French coast two of his ships were taken by English cruisers. A succession of storms scattered the fleet, so that when, after ruinous delays, he sailed into the rendezvous at Chebucto Bay with two ships, he found but one other awaiting him. His mortification brought on a stroke of apoplexy, which soon proved fatal; and fevers thinned the ranks of the troops. Presently Admiral d'Estournelle arrived with other ships, and took command. But on him, too, Fate turned an angry face. He was stricken with insanity, and stabbed himself with his sword. The leadership now fell upon de la Jonquière, a naval officer of distinction who was on his way to Quebec to relieve the governor-general. Meanwhile a few more of the wandering vessels had come straggling into the rendezvous, and Jonquière presently set out to take Annapolis. Ere he reached his destination a **great storm** blew up against him, once more scattering the fleet; and the discouraged remnant sailed away to France." (Source: Charles George Douglas Roberts, *A History of Canada*)

‡**QUEEN ELIZABETH AND THE SPANISH ARMADA** refers to a famous sea battle, in 1588, for sea supremacy between England and Spain. **King Philip of Spain** built "sixty-five large war ships, the smallest of which was seven hundred tons. Seven were over one thousand, and the largest, an Italian ship, *La Regazona*, was thirteen hundred. All were built high like castles, their upper works musket-proof, their main timbers four or five feet thick, and of a strength it was supposed no English cannon could pierce.

"Next to the big ships, or galleons as they were called, were four galeases, each carrying fifty guns and 450 soldiers and sailors, and rowed by 300 slaves. Besides these were four galleys, fifty-six great armed merchant ships, the finest Spain possessed, and twenty caravels, or small vessels. Thus the fighting fleet amounted to 129 vessels, carrying in all 2430 cannon. On board was stored an enormous quantity of provisions for the use of the army after it landed in England, there being sufficient to feed 40,000 men for six months.

"There were on board 8000 sailors, 19,000 soldiers, 1000 gentlemen volunteers, 600 priests, servants, and miscellaneous officers, and 2000 galley slaves. This was indeed a tremendous array to meet the fleet lying off Plymouth, consisting of 29 [of Queen Elizabeth's] ships of all sizes, 10 small vessels belonging to Lord Howard and members of his family, and 43 privateers between 40 and 400 tons under Drake, the united crews amounting to something over 9000 men..." (Source: G.A. Henty, *By England's Aid*)

"[W]ith both sides of the Thames fortified, and with the soldiers under arms, and with the sailors in their ships, [England] waited for the coming of the proud Spanish fleet, which was called "The Invincible Armada". The **Queen** herself, riding in armor on a white horse, and the Earl of Essex and the Earl of Leicester holding her bridal rein, made a brave speech to the troops at Tilbury Fort opposite Gravesend, which was received with such enthusiasm as is seldom known. Then came the Spanish Armada into the English Channel, sailing along in the form of a half moon, of such great size that it was seven miles broad. But the English were quickly upon it, and woe then to all the Spanish ships that dropped a little out of the half moon, for the English took them instantly! And it soon appeared that the great Armada was anything but invincible, for on a summer night, bold Drake sent eight blazing fire-ships right into the midst of it. In terrible consternation the Spaniards tried to get out to sea, and so became dispersed; the English pursued them at a great advantage; **a storm came on**, and drove the Spaniards among rocks and shoals; and the swift end of the Invincible Fleet was, that it lost thirty great ships and ten thousand men, and, defeated and disgraced, sailed home again. Being afraid to go by the English Channel, it sailed all round Scotland and Ireland; some of the ships getting cast away on the latter coast in bad weather, the Irish, who were a kind of savages, plundered those vessels and killed their crews. So ended this great attempt to invade and conquer England." (Source: Charles Dickens, *A Child's History of England*)

†**IMPRESS'**, v.t. [L. impressum, from imprimo; in and premo, to press.] To compel to enter into public service, as seamen; to seize and take into service by compulsion, as nurses in sickness. In this sense, we use press or impress indifferently.

‡**CASTLE WILLIAM**; "[N]ow called Fort Independence." (Source: *A Documentary History of Chelsea*)

Page 159

‡**GENERAL [EDWARD] BRADDOCK**; "Beneath a large tree standing between the heads of the northernmost ravines, and while in the act of giving an order, Braddock received a mortal wound; the ball passing through his right arm into the lungs...Pursued to the water's edge by about fifty savages, the regular troops cast from them guns, accoutrements, and even clothing, that they might run the faster. Many were overtaken and tomahawked here; but when they had once crossed the river, they were not followed...In full possession of his courage and military instincts, Braddock still essayed to procure an orderly and soldier-like retreat; but the demoralization of the army now rendered this impossible...In an hour's time, almost every soldier had stolen away, leaving their officers deserted...men half-famished, without arms, and bewildered with terror...were deserting without ceremony.

"Braddock's strength was now fast ebbing away...He pronounced the warmest eulogiums upon the conduct of his officers (who indeed had merited all he could say of them), and seems to have entertained some compunctions at not having more scrupulously followed the advice of **Washington**...The only allusions he made to the fate of the battle was to softly repeat once or twice to himself–"Who would have thought?" Turning to Orme–"We shall better know how to deal with them another time;" were his parting words. A few moments later, and he breathed his last...The uttermost penalty that humanity could exact, he paid for his errors: and if his misfortune brought death and woe upon his country, it was through no shrinking on his part from what he conceived to be his duty..." (Source: Robert Orme, *The History of an Expedition Against Fort Du Quesne, in 1755 Under Major-General Edward Braddock*)

‡**GEORGE WASHINGTON**; "The preservation of Washington is an anecdote of popular currency. With two horses shot under him and four bullets through his coat, and a special mark for the enemy's rifles, not a single stroke told upon his person. In 1770, on the banks of the Great Kanhawa, an aged chief journeyed from his distant lodge to see once more the favorite of the Great Spirit against whom his

own gun and those of his young men were fifteen years before so often turned in vain. Well might the eloquent Davies express at the time the public conviction that the signal manner in which Providence had hitherto watched over the heroic youth clearly presaged his future importance to his country." (Source: Robert Orme, *The History of an Expedition Against Fort Du Quesne, in 1755 Under Major-General Edward Braddock*)

Page 161

†**QUER'ULOUS**, a. [L. querulus, from queror, to complain. See Quarrel.] Expressing complaint; as a *querulous* tone of voice.

†**EX'ILE**, n. eg'zile. [L. exilium, exul; The word is probably compounded of ex and a root, signifying to depart, or cut off, to separate, or the thrust away, perhaps L. salio.] Banishment; the state of being expelled from one's native country of place of residence by authority, and forbid to return, either for a limited time or for perpetuity.

Page 165

†**ED'IFICE**, n. [L. oedificium. See Edify.] A building; a structure; a fabric; but appropriately, a large or splendid building. The word is not applied to a mean building, but to temples, churches or elegant mansion-houses, and to other great structures.

†**BAL'USTRADE**, n. A row of balusters, joined by a rail, serving as a fence or enclosure, for altars, balconies, staircases, terraces, tops of buildings, &c.

Page 167

‡**"EVANGELINE",** by American poet **Henry Wadsworth Longfellow**, tells the story of a young Acadian girl separated from her love, Gabriel, during the Acadian exile in 1755. She spends her life searching for him without success. Finally, when Gabriel "had become to her heart as one who is dead, and not absent", Evangeline becomes a Sister of Mercy. A plague falls on the city, and one Sabbath morning Evangeline, while tending the afflicted, discovers Gabriel on a sickbed, "the form of an old man". They both recognize each other, and when Evangeline whispered his name,

> Vainly he strove to rise; and Evangeline, kneeling beside him,
> Kissed his dying lips, and laid his head on her bosom
> Sweet was the light of his eyes; but it suddenly sank into darkness,
> As when a lamp is blown out by a gust of wind at a casement.
>
> All was ended now, the hope, and the fear, and the sorrow,
> All the aching of heart, the restless, unsatisfied longing,
> All the dull, deep pain, and constant anguish of patience!
> And, as she pressed once more the lifeless head to her bosom,
> Meekly she bowed her own, and murmured, "Father, I thank thee!"

Page 169

‡**ARMY**; "The soldiers were no soldiers, but farmers and farmers' sons who had volunteered for the summer campaign. One of the corps had a blue uniform faced with red. The rest wore their daily clothing. Blankets and had been served out to them by the several provinces, but the greater part brought their own guns; some under the penalty of a fine if they came without them, and some under the inducement of a reward. They had no bayonets, but carried hatchets in their belts as a sort of substitute. At their sides were slung powder-horns, on which, in the leisure the

camp, they carved quaint devices with the points of their jack-knives. They came chiefly from plain New England homesteads,–rustic abodes, unpainted and dingy, with long well-sweeps, capacious barns, rough fields of pumpkins and corn, and vast kitchen chimneys, above which in winter hung squashes to keep them from frost, and guns to keep them from rust.

"As to the manners and morals of the army there is conflict of evidence. In some respects nothing could be more exemplary. "Not a chicken has been stolen," says William Smith, of New York; while, on the other hand, **Colonel Ephraim Williams** writes to Colonel Israel Williams, then commanding on the Massachusetts frontier: 'We're a wicked, profane army, especially the New York and Rhode Island troops. Nothing to be heard among a great part of them but the language of Hell. If Crown Point is taken, it will not be for our sakes, but for those good people left behind.' There was edifying regularity in respect to form. Sermons twice a week, daily prayers, and frequent psalm-singing alternated with the much-needed military drill. "Prayers among us night and morning," writes private Jonathan Caswell, of Massachusetts, to his father. 'Here we lie, knowing not when we shall march for Crown Point; but I hope not long to tarry. Desiring your prayers to God for me as I am agoing to war, I am Your Ever Dutiful Son.'" (Source: Francis Parkman, *Montcalm and Wolfe: France and England in North America*, Part Seventh)

‡**COLONEL [EPHRAIM] WILLIAMS**; "[W]hen the English advanced to attack the regulars in front, they would find themselves caught in a double ambush. No sight or sound betrayed the snare; but behind every bush crouched a Canadian or a savage, with gun cocked and ears intent, listening for the tramp of the approaching column...It was soon after eight o'clock when Ephraim Williams left the camp with his regiment, marched a little distance, and then waited for the rest of the detachment...Thus **Dieskau** had full time to lay his ambush...In the words of Dieskau, the head of the column 'was doubled up like a pack of cards'...Williams, seeing a rising ground on his right, made for it, calling on his men to follow; but as he climbed the slope, guns flashed from the bushes, and a shot through the brain laid him dead." (Source: Francis Parkman, *Montcalm and Wolfe: France and England in North America*, Part Seventh)

‡**BARON DIESKAU**; "While Johnson lay at Lake George, Dieskau prepared a surprise for him. The German baron had reached Crown Point at the head of 3,573 men, regulars, Canadians, and Indians. He had no thought of waiting there to be attacked. The troops were told to hold themselves ready to move at a moment's notice. Officers–so ran the order–will take nothing with them but one spare shirt, one spare pair of shoes, a blanket, a bearskin, and provisions for twelve days; Indians are not to amuse themselves by taking scalps till the enemy is entirely defeated, since they can kill ten men in the time required to scalp one...The enemy were reported to greatly outnumber him; but his Canadian advisers had assured him that the English colony militia were the worst troops on the face of the earth. 'The more there are,' he said to the Canadians and Indians, 'the more we shall kill'..." (Source: Francis Parkman, *Montcalm and Wolfe: France and England in North America*, Part Seventh)

Page 170

‡**GENERAL [JAMES] ABERCROMBIE**; "Lord Loudoun, from whom so much had been anticipated [as commander of English forces in the American colonies], had disappointed by his inactivity, and been relieved from a command in which he had attempted much and done so little...On the return of his lordship to England, the general command in America devolved on Major-general Abercrombie, and the forces were divided into three detached bodies...[one], under Abercrombie himself, was to proceed against Ticonderoga and Crown Point on Lake Champlain..."

(Source: Washington Irving, *Life of George Washington*)

‡**ILL SUCCESS**; "...**Abercrombie**, a victim to the 'extremest fright and consternation,' hurried the army, that same evening, to the landing-place, with such precipitancy, that but for the alertness of [Colonel John] Bradstreet, it would at once in a mass have rushed into the boats. On the morning of the ninth, he embarked, and did not rest till he had placed the lake between himself and **Montcalm**." (Source: George Bancroft, *History of the United States from the Discovery of the American Continent*)

‡**MARQUIS DE MONTCALM**; [Marquis Louis Joseph de Saint-Veran, known as Montcalm] "The gallant Montcalm had received his death-wound near St. John's Gate, while endeavoring to rally his flying troops, and had been borne into the town...The English had obtained a complete victory, slain about five hundred of the enemy, taken above a thousand prisoners and among them several officers...

"The brave Montcalm wrote a letter to General Townshend, recommending the prisoners to British humanity. When told by his surgeon that he could not survive above a few hours; 'So much the better,' replied he; 'I shall not live to see the surrender of Quebec.' To de Ramsey, the French king's lieutenant, who commanded the garrison, he consigned the defense of the city. 'To your keeping,' said he, 'I commend the honor of France. I'll neither give orders, nor interfere any further. I have business to attend to of greater moment than your ruined garrison, and this wretched country. My time is short–I shall pass this night with God, and prepare myself for death. I wish you all comfort; and to be happily extricated from you present perplexities.' He then called for his chaplain, who, with the bishop of the colony, remained with him through the night. He expired early in the morning, dying like a brave soldier and a devout Catholic. Never did two worthier foes mingle their life blood on the battlefield than **Wolfe** and Montcalm." (Source: Washington Irving, *Life of George Washington*)

Page 172

‡**GENERAL [JAMES] WOLFE**; "General Wolfe was a great admirer of the poet Gray. As he went the rounds for final inspection on the beautiful starlight evening before the attack, he remarked to those in the boat with him, 'I would rather be the author of 'The Elegy in a Country Churchyard', than to have the glory of beating the French tomorrow'; and amid the rippling of the water and the dashing of the oars, he repeated:

> The boast of heraldry, the pomp of power,
> And all that beauty, all that wealth e'er gave,
> Await alike the inevitable hour;
> The paths of glory lead but to the grave."

(Source: Joel Dorman Steele, *A Brief History of the United States*)

‡**GREAT FIRE OF BOSTON**; "Among the ten so-called 'Great Fires'..., that of 1760 destroyed 349 buildings, among them many dwelling-houses, rendering a thousand people homeless; that of 1711 destroyed the Town House, the old meeting-house of the First Church, and 100 dwellings; in 1702 what was a large amount of property for those days was burned in the seventh 'Great Fire,' and 'three warehouses were blown up to hinder its spreading;' and in 1679 all the warehouses and many dwelling-houses with the vessels then in the dock were consumed; and **Mather** wrote of this calamity, 'Ah, Boston! Thou hast seen the vanity of all worldly possessions. One fatal morning, which laid fourscore of thy dwelling-houses and seventy of thy warehouses in a ruinous heap, gave thee to read it in fiery characters.' Three years before, in 1676, another great fire burned 46 dwelling-houses and other buildings,

including 'a meeting-house of considerable bigness.'" (Source: Edwin Monroe Bacon, *Bacon's Dictionary of Boston*)

Page 176

†**PALLA'DIUM**, n. [Gr. from Pallas, the goddess.] Primarily, a statue of the goddess Pallas, which represented her as sitting with a pike in her right hand, and in her left a distaff and spindle. On the preservation of this statue depended the safety of Troy. Hence, something that affords effectual defense, protection and safety; as when we say, the trial by jury is the *palladium* of our civil rights.

Page 177

†**PON'DEROUS**, a. [L. ponderosus.] Very heavy; weighty; as a *ponderous* shield; a *ponderous* load.

Page 178

‡**BANCROFT**; Probably referring to George Bancroft, author of the ten volume *History of the United States of America, From the Discovery of the Continent*. See page 48 for another reference to Bancroft.

Page 179

†**MON'ARCHIST**, n. An advocate of monarchy

MON'ARCHY, n. [Gr.] A state or government in which the supreme power is lodged in the hands of a single person. Such a state is usually called an empire or a kingdom; and we usually give this denomination to a large state only. But the same name is sometimes given to a kingdom or state in which the power of the king or supreme magistrate is limited by a constitution, or by fundamental laws. Such is the British *monarchy*. Hence we speak of absolute or despotic *monarchies*, and of limited *monarchies*.

†**REPUB'LICAN**, a. Pertaining to a republic; consisting of a commonwealth; as a *republican* constitution or government.

REPUB'LIC, n. [L. respublica; res and publica; public affairs.] A commonwealth; a state in which the exercise of the sovereign power is lodged in representatives elected by the people. In modern usage, it differs from a democracy or democratic state, in which the people exercise the powers of sovereignty in person. Yet the democracies of Greece are often called republics.

†**SUF'FRAGE**, n. [L. suffragium.] A vote; a voice given in deciding a controverted question, or in the choice of a man for an office or trust. Nothing can be more grateful to a good man than to be elevated to office by the unbiased *suffrages* of free enlightened citizens.

†**BOON**, n. [L. bonus.] A gift; a grant; a benefaction; a present; a favor granted.

†**EMOL'UMENT**, n. [L. emolumentum, from emolo, molo, to grind. Originally, toll taken for grinding.] The profit arising from office or employment; that which is received as a compensation for services, or which is annexed to the possession of office, as salary, feels and perquisites.

Page 180

†**REV'ERIE**, n. Properly, a raving or delirium; but its sense, as generally used, is a loose or irregular train of thoughts, occurring in musing or meditation; wild,

extravagant conceit of the fancy or imagination. There are *reveries* and extravagancies which pass through the minds of wise men as well as fools.

†**ENTA'IL**, v.t. To settle the descent of lands and tenements, by gift to a man and to certain heirs specified, so that neither the donee nor any subsequent possessor can alienate or bequeath it; as, to *entail* a manor to AB and to his eldest son, or to his heirs of his body begotten, or to his heirs by a particular wife. To fix unalienably on a person or thing, or on a person and his descendants. By the apostasy misery is supposed to be *entailed* on mankind. The intemperate often *entail* infirmities, diseases and ruin on their children.

†**ION'IC**, a. [from Ionia.] The Ionic order, in architecture, is that species of column named from Ionia, in Greece. It is more slender than the Doric and Tuscan, but less slender and less ornamented than the Corinthian and Composite. It is simple, but majestic; its height is 18 modules, and that of the entablature four and a half.

Page 181

†**AMBIG'UOUS**, a. [L. ambiguus.] Having two or more meanings; doubtful; being of uncertain signification; susceptible of different interpretations; hence, obscure. It is applied to words and expressions; not to a dubious state of mind, though it may be to a person using words of doubtful signification.

†**PER'EMPTORY**, a. [L. peremptorius, from peremptus, taken away, killed.] Express; positive; absolute; decisive; authoritative; in a manner to preclude debate or expostulation. The orders of the commander are *peremptory*.

†**IMPLIC'IT**, a. [L. implicitus, from implico, supra.] Implied; tacitly comprised; fairly to be understood, though not expressed in words; as an *implicit* contract or agreement.

Page 182

†**ANIMADVERT'**, v.i. [L. animadverto, of animus, mind, and adverto, to turn to.] To consider or remark upon by way of criticism or censure.

†**FOR'FEIT**, v.t. for'fit. [Low L. forisfacere, from L. foris, out or abroad, and facio, to make.] To lose or render confiscable, by some fault, offense or crime; to lose the right to some species of property or that which belongs to one; to alienate the right to possess by some neglect or crime; as, to *forfeit* an estate by a breach of the condition of tenure or by treason. By the ancient laws of England, a man *forfeited* his estate by neglecting or refusing to fulfill the conditions on which it was granted to him, or by a breach of fealty. A man now *forfeits* his estate by committing treason. A man *forfeits* his honor or reputation by a breach of promise, and by any criminal or disgraceful act. Statutes declare that by certain acts a man shall *forfeit* a certain sum of money.

†**PER'EMPTORILY**, adv. [from peremptory.] Absolutely; positively; in a decisive manner; so as to preclude further debate.

†**DISCOMMODE**, v.t. To put to inconvenience; to incommode; to molest; to trouble.

†**MOLEST'**, v.t. [L. molestus, troublesome, molo.] To trouble; to disturb; to render uneasy.

Page 184

†**OB'STINACY**, n. [L. obstinatio, from obsto, to stand against, to oppose; ob and sto.] A fixedness in opinion or resolution that cannot be shaken at all, or not without

great difficulty; firm and usually unreasonable adherence to an opinion, purpose or system; a fixedness that will not yield to persuasion, arguments or other means. Obstinacy may not always convey the idea of unreasonable or unjustifiable firmness; as when we say, soldiers fight with *obstinacy*. But often, and perhaps usually, the word denotes a fixedness of resolution which is not to be vindicated under the circumstances; stubbornness; pertinacity; persistency.

†**TEMER'ITY**, n. [L. temeritas; properly a rushing forward.] Rashness; unreasonable contempt of danger; as the *temerity* of a commander in war. Extreme boldness.

†**PERFID'IOUS**, a. [L. perfidus; per and fidus, faithful. 'Per' in this word signifies through, beyond, or by, aside.] Violating good faith or vows; false to trust or confidence reposed; treacherous; as a *perfidious* agent; a perfidious friend. Guilty of violated allegiance; as a *perfidious* citizen; a man *perfidious* to his country.

†**SU'RETY**, n. Certainty; indubitableness. *Security* against loss or damage; *security* for payment.

†**EMBARKA'TION**, n. The act of putting on board of a ship or other vessel, or the act of going aboard.

Page 189

†**ANON'**, adv. Quickly; without intermission: soon; immediately.

Page 193

‡**KING GEORGE III**; "As far as can be discerned of the King's natural disposition, it was humane and benevolent...His childhood was tinctured with obstinacy: it was adopted at the beginning of his reign, and called firmness; but did not prove to be his complexion. In truth, it would be difficult to draw his character in positive colors. He had neither passions nor activity. He resigned himself obsequiously to the government of his mother and Lord Bute: learned, and even entered with art into the lessons they inspired, but added nothing of his own. When the task was done, he relapsed into indifference and indolence, till roused to the next day's part. (When Prince of Wales, Scott, his sub-preceptor, reproached him with inattention to his studies, the prince pleaded idleness. 'Idle! Sir,' said Scott; 'your brother Edward is idle; but do you call being asleep, being idle?')" (Source: Horace Walpole, *Memoirs of the Reign of King George the Third*)

†**SAGA'CIOUS**, a. [L. sagax, from sagus, wise, foreseeing; saga, a wise woman; sagio, to perceive readily. The latter signifies wise, prudent, sage, and an essay, which unites this word with seek, and L. sequor.] Quick of thought; acute in discernment or penetration; as a *sagacious* head; a *sagacious* mind.

Page 195

‡**STAMP ACT**; **George Grenville**, prime minister of England, "gave notice that he intended to lay a tax on the colonies to help defray the expense of a small standing army in America. The proposal seemed reasonable, for at the very moment English troops west of Alleghenies were engaged in the serious business of quelling an **Indian uprising**, headed by the Ottawa chief Pontiac, who, not accepting the peace of 1763, had united all the tribes from the Illini to the Seneca's in a last determined effort to keep the English out of the Ohio valley. According to the preamble of the act, the money which the ministry proposed to raise in American was to be spent in America, and the colonies were to be asked to contribute only about a third of the sum necessary. Furthermore, Grenville, who had no wish to offend the colonies, was willing to assess the tax in the way most acceptable to the Americans. He

himself proposed a stamp tax, which required that all official and public documents, such as wills, deeds, mortgages, notes, newspapers, pamphlets, should be written on stamped paper or provided with stamps sold by the distributing agents of the British government; but at the same time he invited the colonial agents in London and influential men in the colonies to suggest any other form of taxation which appeared to them more suitable or acceptable, and announced that no definite action in the matter would be taken for a year.

"No other plan was considered, and in March, 1765, the Stamp Act was passed with very little discussion, and a half-filled Parliament, by a vote of 205 to 49. Distributors of stamped paper were appointed for the colonies, **Benjamin Franklin** even soliciting the position in Pennsylvania for one of his friends. The British ministry anticipated no resistance to the act, which was to go into effect the first of November." (Source: David Saville Muzzey, *An American History*)

Page 196

†**TRIB'UTARY**, a. [from tribute.] Paying tribute to another, either from compulsion, as an acknowledgment of submission, or to secure protection, or for the purpose of purchasing peace. Subject; subordinate.

†**DELEGATE**, n. A person appointed and sent by another with powers to transact business as his representative; a deputy; a commissioner; a vicar. In the United States, a person elected or appointed to represent a state or a district, in the Congress, or in a Convention for forming or altering a constitution.

Page 197

†**REMON'STRANCE**, n. Expostulation; strong representation of reasons against a measure, either public or private, and when addressed to a public body, a prince or magistrate, it may be accompanied with a petition or supplication for the removal or prevention of some evil or inconvenience.

†**PETI'TION**, n. [L. petitio, from peto, to ask, properly to urge or press.] A formal request or supplication, verbal or written; particularly, a written supplication from an inferior to a superior, either to a single person clothed with power, or to a legislative or other body, soliciting some favor, grant, right or mercy.

†**PRU'DENT**, a. Cautious; circumspect; practically wise; careful of the consequences of enterprises, measures or actions; cautious not to act when the end is of doubtful utility, or probably impracticable.

Page 198

‡**LIBERTY TREE**; "At daybreak on the 14th August, 1765, nearly ten years before active hostilities broke out, an effigy of **Mr. [Andrew] Oliver**, the Stamp officer, and a boot, with the Devil peeking out of it, –an allusion to **Lord Bute**,–were discovered hanging from Liberty Tree. The images remained hanging all day, and were visited by a great numbers of people, both from the town and the neighboring country. Business was almost suspended. Lieutenant-Governor Hutchinson ordered the sheriff to take the figures down, but he was obliged to admit that he dared not do so.

"As the day closed in the effigies were taken down, placed upon a bier, and, followed by several thousand people of every class and condition, preceded first to the Town House, and from thence to the supposed office of the Stamp Master... With materials obtained from the ruins of the building, the procession moved to Fort Hill, where a bonfire was lighted and the effigies consumed in full view of

Mr. Oliver's house. **Governor Bernard** and council were in session in the Town House when the procession passed through it, as the lower floor of the building left open for public promenade permitted them to do. In the attacks which followed upon the houses of the secretary, lieutenant-governor, and officers of the admiralty, Mackintosh appears to have been the leader. In these proceedings the records of the court of vice-admiralty were destroyed,–an irreplaceable loss to the province and to history. Mackintosh was arrested, but immediately released on the demand of a number of persons of character and property." (Source: Samuel Adams Drake, *Old Landmarks and Historic Personages of Boston*)

†**EF'FIGY**, n. [L. effigies, from effingo, to fashion; ex and fingo, to form or devise.] The image or likeness of a person; resemblance; representation; any substance fashioned into the shape of a person. To burn or **hang in effigy**, is to burn or hang an image or picture of the person intended to be executed, disgraced or degraded. In France, when a criminal cannot be apprehended, his picture is hung on a gallows or gibbet, at the bottom of which is written his sentence of condemnation.

Page 201

†**PILAS'TER**, n. A square column, sometimes insulated; but usually pilasters are set within a wall, projecting only one quarter of their diameter. Their bases, capitals and entablatures have the same parts as those of columns.

Page 203

†**TU'MULT**, n. [L. tumultus, a derivative from tumeo, to swell.] The commotion, disturbance or agitation of a multitude, usually accompanied with great noise, uproar and confusion of voices.

Page 205

†**CONCOURSE**, n. [L., to run together, to run.] A moving, flowing or running together; confluence; as a fortuitous *concourse* of atoms; a *concourse* of men.

Page 209

†**EQUINOC'TIAL**, a. [L. oequus, equal, and nox, night.] Pertaining to the time when the sun enters the equinoctial points; as an *equinoctial* gale or storm, which happens at or near the equinox, in any part of the world.

Page 210

‡**MR. [ANDREW] OLIVER**; "[T]he greatest act which occurred under this famous tree was the public declaration of Secretary Oliver that he would not in any way, by himself or by deputy, perform the duties of stamp master. The Secretary, desirous of less publicity, had requested that the ceremony might take place at the Town House, but the 'Sons' had determined that the 'Tree' was the proper place, and Mr. Oliver presented himself there. Besides this declaration, subscribed to before Richard Dana, justice of the peace, Mr. Oliver fully recanted his sentiments in favor of the Stamp Act, and desired the people no longer to look upon him as an enemy, but as a friend,–a piece of duplicity fully exposed by the discovery of his correspondence on the subject." (Source: Samuel Adams Drake, *Old Landmarks and Historic Personages of Boston*)

Page 211

†**INCLEM'ENCY**, n. [L. inclementia. See Clemency.] 1. Want of clemency; want of mildness of temper; unmercifulness; harshness; severity; applied to persons. 2.

Roughness, boisterousness; storminess; or simply raininess; severe cold, &c.; applied to the weather. We were detained by the *inclemency* of the weather.

‡**BRITISH COFFEE HOUSE**; The British Coffee House was "...an inn kept by Mr. Ballard in 1762. It was of some prominence, and divided with its neighbors the patronage of the military and civilians. The repeal of the Stamp Act was celebrated here...It was also the scene of the unfortunate collision between **James Otis** and John Robinson, one of the Customs Commissioners referred to in connection with Otis's residence. Otis went to the Coffee House alone, by appointment, and was immediately attacked by Robinson and his friends. A young man who went to the assistance of Otis was roughly handled and put out of the house.

"The house seems to have been preferred by British officers; for we find one of them, Surgeon Bolton, delivering a harangue from the balcony, ridiculing the orations of Warren and Hancock, and abusive of the Whig patriots, while the main-guard, paraded in front, furnished an audience. Under the new *régime* this tavern was styled the American Coffee House. It became a place of public vendue, in 1786, by a firm who sold books in the chamber and jackasses in the street. The Massachusetts Bank long occupied the site." (Source: Samuel Adams Drake, *Old Landmarks and Historic Personages of Boston*)

Page 213

†**RED'COAT**, n. A name given to a soldier who wears a red coat.

†**SENT'INEL**, n. [from L. sentio, to perceive.] In military affairs, a soldier sent to watch or guard an army, camp or other place from surprise, to observe the approach of danger and give notice of it. In popular sense, the word is contracted into sentry.

Page 214

†**TO'RY**, n. [said to be an Irish word, denoting a robber; perhaps from tor, a bush, as the Irish banditti lived in the mountains or among trees.] The name given to an adherent to the ancient constitution of England and to the apostolical hierarchy. The Tories form a party which are charged with supporting more arbitrary principles in government than the Whigs, their opponents. In America, during the revolution, those who opposed the war, and favored the claims of Great Britain, were called Tories.

†**CUSTOMHOUSE**, n. The house where vessel enter and clear, and where the customs are paid or secured to be paid.

†**YANKEE**, n. A corrupt pronunciation of the word English by the native Indians of America.

Page 216

‡**GERMAN BOY**; A different version of this event is thus told: a loyalist merchant, Theophilus Lillie "announced his intention to import and sell tea in spite of public opinion. That opinion soon appeared embodied in a little mob, composed chiefly of half-grown boys, who set up a wooden post in front of Lillie's store, with a rudely carved head upon it, and a hand pointing to the merchant's store as a place to be avoided. Lillie was exasperated, but dared not interfere. A neighboring merchant of his stripe, named Richardson, a rough, stout man, having more courage, tried to get a farmer, who was passing in his cart, to knock down the post with his hub. The man was a patriot and refused, when Richardson rushed out and attempted to pull it down with his own hands. He was pelted with dirt and stones. In a violent anger,

he came out of Lillie's house, into which he had been driven by the mob, with a shotgun, and discharged its contents, without aim, into the little mob. A lad named Samuel Gore was slightly wounded, and another, named **Christopher Snyder**, was killed. He was the son of a poor German widow. The mob seized Richardson and an associate and hurried them to **Faneuil Hall,** where the citizens speedily assembled to the number of two or three hundred. Richardson was tried and found guilty of murder, but **Lieutenant-Governor Hutchinson** refused to sign the death warrant. After he had lain in prison for two years, the king pardoned the offender.

"The murder of Snyder produced a profound sensation in the public mind throughout the colonies, as a prophecy of coming war. In Boston his funeral was made the occasion of a solemn pageant. His coffin was covered with inscriptions. One of them was: 'Innocence itself is not safe.' It was born to **Liberty Tree**, where a very large concourse of citizens of every class assembled, and followed the remains to the grave. In the procession nearly 500 children took part. The pall was carried by six of the victim's schoolmates. Relatives and friends of almost 1500 citizens followed. The bells of the city and of neighboring towns tolled while the procession was moving; and in the newspapers, and by the lips of grave speakers in the pulpit and on the rostrum, little Christopher Snyder was spoken of as the first martyr to the cause of liberty in America." (Source: Benson John Lawson, *Our Country*)

Page 217

†**AFFRA'Y**, n. In law, the fighting of two or more persons, in a public place, to the terror of others. A fighting in private is not, in a legal sense, an affray. Tumult; disturbance.

Page 218

†**EN'MITY**, n. The quality of being an enemy; the opposite of friendship; ill-will; hatred; unfriendly dispositions; malevolence. It expresses more than aversion and less than malice, and differs from displeasure in denoting a fixed or rooted hatred, whereas displeasure is more transient.

Page 219

‡**CRISPUS ATTUCKS**; "On March 5, 1770, occurred the **Boston Massacre**; and, while it was not the real commencement of the Revolutionary struggle, it was the bloody drama that opened the most eventful and thrilling chapter in American history.... There is no record to controvert the fact of the leadership of Crispus Attucks. A manly-looking fellow, six feet two inches in height, he was a commanding figure among the irate colonists. His enthusiasm for the threatened interests of the Province, his loyalty to the teachings of Otis, and his willingness to sacrifice for the cause of equal rights, endowed him with a courage, which, if tempered with better judgment, would have made him a military hero in his day...Attucks led the charge with the shout, 'The way to get rid of these soldiers is to attack the main-guard; strike at the root: this is the nest.' A shower of missiles was answered by the discharge of the guns...the exposed and commanding person of the intrepid Attucks went down before the murderous fire." (Source: George Washington Williams, *History of the Negro Race in America from 1619 to 1880*)

Page 221

†**PRESENT'IMENT**, n. [pre and sentiment.] Previous conception, sentiment or opinion; previous apprehension of something future.

Page 227

‡**BOSTON MASSACRE**; "I, Charles Hobby, of lawful age, testify and say, that on Monday evening the 5th instant, between the hours of nine and ten o'clock, beating my master's house, was alarmed with the cry of fire, and ran down as far as the town-house, and then heard that the soldiers and the inhabitants were fighting in the alley by Doctor Cooper's meeting-house. I went through the alley, I there saw a number of soldiers about the barracks, some with muskets, others without. I saw a number of officers at the door of the mess-house, almost fronting the alley, and some of the inhabitants entreating the officers to command the soldiers to be peaceable and retire to their barracks. One of the officers, viz., Lieutenant Minchin, replied, that the soldiers had been abused lately by the inhabitants, and that if the inhabitants would disperse, the soldiers should follow their example. Captain Goldfinch was among the rest of the officers in or about the steps of the mess-house door, but did not command the soldiers. I then left them and went King Street. I then saw a party of soldiers loading their muskets about the Custom-house door, after which they all shouldered. I heard some of the inhabitants cry out, "Heave no snowballs;" others cried "They dare not fire." Caption Preston was then standing by the soldiers, when a snowball struck a grenadier, who immediately fired, Captain Preston standing close by him. The Captain then spoke distinctly, "Fire! Fire!" I was then within four feet of Captain Preston, and know him well; the soldiers fired as fast as they could one after another. I saw the mulatto fall [*likely* **Crispus Attucks**–*Ed. note*], and Mr. Samuel Gray went look at him, one of the soldiers, at that distance of about four or five yards, pointed his piece directly for the said Gray' head and fired. Mr. Gray, after struggling, turned himself right around upon his heel and fell dead. Captain Preston some time after ordered them to march to the guard-house. I then took up a round hat and followed the people that carried him down to a house near the post-office. And further saith not. –Charles Hobby" (Source: Printed by order of the town of Boston, *A Short Narrative of the Horrid Massacre in Boston*)

Page 228

†**AS'TRAL**, a. [L. astrum; Gr. a star.] Belonging to the stars; starry.

Page 230

†**COURTIER**, n. [from court.] A man who attends or frequents the courts of princes.

‡**KING'S PROCLAMATION**; "The British force in Boston was increasing by fresh arrivals. It numbered then about 10,000 men. Generals **Howe**, Clinton, and **Burgoyne** had arrived late in May, and heartily joined **Gage** in forming and executing plans for dispersing the 'rebels.' Feeling strong with these veteran officers and soldiers around him, and the presence of several ships-of-war under Admiral Graves, the governor issued a most insulting proclamation, declaring martial law, branding those citizens in arms, and their abettors, as 'rebels' and 'parricides of the Constitution,' and offering pardon to all who should forthwith return to their allegiance, excepting **Samuel Adams** and **John Hancock**, who were reserved for condign punishment as traitors. This proclamation produced intense indignation throughout the province. 'All the records of time," wrote Mrs. John Adams to her husband, "cannot produce a blacker page. Satan, when driven from the regions of bliss, exhibited not more malice. Surely the father of lies is superseded. Yet we think it is the best proclamation he could have issued." (Source: Benson John Lossing, *Our Country*)

Page 231

‡**JOSEPH WARREN**; "General Warren had come upon the field, as he said, to learn the art of war from a veteran soldier. He had offered to take Colonel Prescott's orders [to retreat at Bunker's Hill]; but his desperate courage would hardly permit him to obey the last. It was not without extreme reluctance, and at the very latest moment, that he quitted the redoubt; and he was slowly retreating from it, being still at a few rods' distance only, when the British had obtained full possession. He person was, of course, in imminent danger. At this critical moment, Major Small, whose life...had been saved in a similar emergency by the interference of **General Putnam**, attempted to requite the service by rendering one of a like character to Warren. He called out to him by name from the redoubt, and begged him to surrender, at the same time ordering the men around him to suspend their fire. Warren turned his head, as if he recognized the voice, but the effort was too late. While his face was directed toward the works, a ball struck him on the forehead, and inflicted a wound which was instantly fatal...**General Howe**, though slightly wounded in the foot, passed the night on the field of battle. The next morning, as he lay wrapped in his cloak upon a mound of hay, word was brought to him, that the body of Warren was found among the dead. Howe refused, at first, to credit the intelligence. It was impossible, that the President of Congress could have exposed his life in such a battle. When assured of the fact, he declared that his death was a full offset for the loss of five hundred men." (Source: Jared Sparks, *The Library of American Biography*, Vol. X)

‡**SPARKS**; Likely referring to *The Works of Benjamin Franklin* by Jared Sparks.

Page 231

‡**JUDGE AUCHMUTY**; "Early in March came the anniversary of the **Boston massacre**. Two days before, Judge Auchmuty, in Boston, wrote to **Hutchinson**: 'I don't see any reason to expect peace and order until the fatal experiment of arms is tried... Bloodshed and desolation seem inevitable.'" (Source: Justin Winsor, *Narrative and Critical History of America*)

Page 235

†**INGEN'UOUSLY**, adv. Openly; fairly; candidly; without reserve or dissimulation.

Page 236

‡**KING GEORGE THE THIRD**; "For two generations England had been ruled chiefly by Parliament. The first two Georges had little to do with the management of the empire, and less with that of the colonies. But when George III came to the throne, 1760, he took the reins of government into his own hands. Often had he heard this mandate of his mother, 'George, be King!' It was no easy task to get Parliament to yield to his will. But, by bribes in money and by the appointment of many members of Parliament and their friends to good offices, he secured control of a majority in Parliament, who worked with him to further his schemes. George III was self-willed, arbitrary, and determined to rule England and the colonies in his own way, without regard for the wishes of the people. With his bribed Parliament, he soon began to modify old laws, to enact new ones, and to enforce obedience to the laws, and thus drove the colonies first into union, then into rebellion." (Source: E. G. Foster, *A History of the United States*)

†**PHYSIOG'NOMY**, n. [Gr. nature, and knowing; to know.] The art or science of discerning the character of the mind from the features of the face; or the art of discovering the predominant temper or other characteristic qualities of the mind by the form of the body, but especially by the external signs of the countenance, or the

combination of the features.

Page 240

‡**GREATLY ENRAGED**; Massachusetts irritated **King George III**. "In King George's eyes the '**Boston Tea Party**' was the last straw; the colonies had added insult to injury. The King called upon Parliament for severe measures of punishment. Massachusetts, especially Boston, must be made an example of the royal vengeance to the rest of the colonies; the province was an old offender. As early as 1646 the general court had assembled for the 'discussion of the usurpation of Parliament,' and a spirited member had declared that 'if England should impose laws upon us we should lose the liberties of Englishmen indeed.'...Since the very first attempt of the British government after the **French war** to tighten its control of colonial commerce and raise a revenue in America, Massachusetts had taken the leading part in defiance. Letters, pamphlets, petitions, came in an uninterrupted stream from the Massachusetts patriots, **Hancock**, **Warren**, **Otis**, and **Adamses**. It was in Boston that the chief resistance to the **Stamp Act** had been offered (1765); it was there also that the King had stationed his regiment of regulars (1768), and there that occurred the unfortunate '**massacre**' of the fifth of March (1770). 'To George III's eyes the capital of Massachusetts was the center of vulgar sedition, strewn with brickbats and broken glass, where his enemies went about clothed in homespun and his friends in tar and feathers.'" (Source: David Saville Muzzey, *An American History*)

Page 241

†**CONTINENTAL**, a. Pertaining or relating to a continent; as the *continental* powers of Europe. In America, pertaining to the United States, as *continental* money, in distinction from what pertains to the separate states; a word much used during the revolution.

†**PROVIN'CIAL**, a. Pertaining to a province or relating to it; as a *provincial* government; a provincial dialect.

Page 242

‡...**SOON TO BE PROVED**; "The **minutemen** were thoroughly familiar with the country and used their knowledge to good purpose. From every wall and tree, from every thicket and hill–'spots which the genius of **Hawthorne** and Emerson have converted into shrines'–a deadly fire was kept up. The weary [British] soldiers were forced to abandon some of their dead and dying and 'huddled along the road like sheep beset by dogs.' No sooner had they passed one dangerous point than the Massachusetts farmers took some short cut and, from another point of vantage, renewed the attack. 'They seemed to drop from the skies,' said one of the survivors. 'We began to run rather than retreat in order,' said another. The day was unusually warm, and when, about two o'clock, the retreating column met Percy just east of Lexington, the men were likened to dogs with their tongues hanging out of their mouths." (Source: Elroy McKendree Avery, *A History of the United States and Its People: From Their Earliest Records to the Present Time*)

†**YEOMANRY**, n. The collective body of yeomen or freeholders. Thus the common people in America, are called yeomanry.

Page 243

‡...**BEGAN THE WAR OF THE REVOLUTION**; Noting much night time activity, a British officer "became worried, sent back to Boston for reinforcements to beat these farmers at whom he and his friends had scoffed so often, and ordered **Major [John] Pitcairn** forward to **Lexington** with six light companies, still hopeful of surprise.

Major Pitcairn picks up everybody he meets, to prevent alarm being given; but one Bowman, and active and diligent person, as it would seem, and a brave soldier of the last French war, eludes him, rides hotly to Lexington, and warns the **minute-men**, who have been waiting since two o'clock [after being warned by **Paul Revere** that the British were coming], and had almost come to believe that the British were not advancing at all. So when Major Pitcairn got to Lexington Green, about half past four, thanks to Bowman's warning, there were some sixty or seventy men assembled to meet him. 'Disperse, ye rebels; disperse!' cried Major Pitcairn, and rode toward them. There was much discussion then, and there has been much more since, as to who fired first. It matters not. It is certain that the British poured in a volley and followed it up with others." (Henry Cabot Lodge, *The Story of the Revolution*)

Page 244

‡**DIORAMA OF BUNKER HILL**; "On the 14th of June, 1841, the Boston Museum and Gallery of Fine Arts was opened by Mr. Moses Kimball and associates, in the building erected for the purpose at the corner of Tremont and Bromfield streets. The collection of natural curiosities [included]...Major Stevens' Diorama of the **Battle of Bunker Hill**..." (Source: William Warland Clapp, *Record of the Boston Stage*)

Page 246

†**RECONNOIT'RE**, v.t. To view; to survey; to examine by the eye; particularly in military affairs, to examine the state of an enemy's army or camp, or the ground for military operations.

Page 248

‡**...BETTER ORDER AND DISCIPLINE**; "The popular army was unorganized, divided into separate bands quite independent of each other, undisciplined, and unled. Hence the ultimate defeat which prevision, organization, and tenacity of purpose would have so easily prevented. What the people could do fighting for themselves and their own rights was plain. Equally plain was the point where they failed. Could they redeem this failure and eradicate the cause of it? Could the popular force be organized, disciplined, trained, and made subordinate to a single purpose? In other words, could it produce a leader, recognize him when found, concentrate in him all the power and meaning it had, rise out of anarchy and chaos into order and light, and follow one man through victory and defeat to ultimate triumph? These were really the great questions before the American people when the smoke had cleared and the bodies had been borne away from the slopes of Breed's Hill [after the battle of **Bunker Hill**]." (Source: Henry Cabot Lodge, The Story of the Revolution)

Page 250

†**INTEG'RITY**, n. [L. integritas, from integer.] 1. Wholeness; entireness; unbroken state. The constitution of the U. States guaranties to each state the *integrity* of its territories. The contracting parties guarantied the *integrity* of the empire. 2. The entire, unimpaired state of any thing, particularly of the mind; moral soundness or purity; incorruptness; uprightness; honesty. Integrity comprehends the whole moral character, but has a special reference to uprightness in mutual dealings, transfers of property, and agencies for others. 3. Purity; genuine, unadulterated, unimpaired state; as the *integrity* of language.

Page 253

‡**VIOLENT GALE AND STORM**; "**Sir William [Howe]** meant to effect a landing

under cover of the night. Besides the twenty thousand men under arms along the American lines, the hills overlooking the scene of expected combat were black with spectators. Without quitting their posts of observation, they awaited in breathless anxiety throughout the morning, the afternoon, until the tide had ebbed too far for boats to reach the shore in front of the American entrenchments. In the evening the British transports, accompanied by a floating battery, dropped down to the Castle; but during the night a furious **gale** rendered a landing out of the question. Three of the transports were blown ashore on Governor's Island. The Americans were subjected to much discomfort throughout the night, being compelled to bivouac, exposed to the whole violence of the storm. The works were, however, so much strengthened by daybreak of the 6th as to render an attack improbable.

"In effect, the storm having frustrated his design, and seeing the hostile works hourly growing under his eyes, Howe, on the 6th, called a council of war, which determined on the evacuation of the place." (Source: Samuel Adams Drake, *History of Middlesex County*)

Page 253

‡**GENERAL CHARLES LEE**; In spring of 1776, "**Washington** tried to defend New York, but [the British] superior force of veterans...compelled him to retreat step by step through the city of New York and up the Hudson, then across the river into New Jersey, and then across the state of New Jersey to a safe position on the western bank of the Delaware. With 3000 men left in the hands of the British as prisoners, and 7000 more under the command of the insubordinate and treacherous Charles Lee refusing to come to his aid, Washington wrote to his brother in December: 'If every nerve is not strained to recruit a new army with all possible expedition, I think the game is pretty nearly up.'" Later, in the summer of 1778, British forces evacuating Philadelphia escaped defeat "...only by the treachery of General Charles Lee, who basely ordered a retreat at the battle of Monmouth. Washington arrived on the scene of action in time to save the day for the American cause, and sent Lee into long-merited disgrace." (Source: David Saville Muzzey, *An American History*)

‡**...HE WHO KILLED THE WOLF**; "This, of course, is that famous encounter with the wolf, which has since become part and parcel not only of local tradition, but of American history...it will now be told in the language of a contemporary, Colonel David Humphrey, who was an aide-de-camp to **General Putnam**, and also to **General Washington**, during the Revolutionary War...

'[As a young man, General Putman farmed in Connecticut.] In one night he had seventy fine sheep and goats killed, besides many lambs and kids wounded. This havoc was committed by a she-wolf, which, with her annual whelps, had for several years infested the vicinity...Farmer Putnam entered into a combination with five of his neighbors to hunt alternately until they could destroy her...The people soon collected, with dogs, guns, straw, fire, and sulphur, to attack the common enemy, and made several unsuccessful efforts to force her from [her] den...Wearied with the fruitless attempts (which had brought the time to ten o'clock at night), Mr. Putnam tried once more to make his dog enter, but in vain. Then he proposed to his Negro man to go down into the cavern and shoot the wolf; but he declined the hazardous service. Then it was that the master resolved himself to destroy the ferocious beast, lest she should escape through some unknown fissure of the rock. His neighbors strongly remonstrated against the perilous enterprise; but he, knowing that wild animals were intimidated by fire, and having provided several strips of birch-bark, the only combustible material he could obtain that would afford light in this deep and darksome cave, prepared for his descent. Having accordingly divested himself of his coat and waistcoat, and having a long rope fastened about his legs, by which he might be pulled back at a concerted signal, he entered head foremost, with the blazing torch in his hand...

'Having groped his passage to the horizontal part of the den, he found it dark and silent as the house of death. He, cautiously proceeding onward, came to the ascent, which he slowly mounted on his hands and knees until he discovered the glaring eyeballs of the wolf, who was crouching at the extremity of the cavern. Startled by the sight of fire, she gnashed her teeth and gave a sullen growl. Having made the necessary discovery (that the wolf was in the den), Putnam kicked at the rope, as a signal for pulling him out. The people at the mouth of the den, who had listened with painful anxiety, hearing the growling of the wolf, and supposing their friend to be in the most imminent danger, drew him forth with such celerity that his shirt was stripped over his head and his skin severely lacerated.

'After adjusting his clothes, and loading his gun with nine buckshot, holding a torch in one hand and the musket in the other, he descended the second time. He drew nearer than before, and the wolf, assuming a still more fierce and terrible appearance, growling, rolling her eyes, snapping her teeth, and dropping her head between her legs, was evidently on the point of springing at him. At this critical instant he leveled his gun and fired at her head. Stunned with the shock and suffocated with the smoke, he immediately found himself drawn out of the cave. But, having refreshed himself, and permitted the smoke to dissipate, he went down the third time. Once more he came within sight of the wolf, who appearing very passive, he applied the torch to her nose, and perceiving her dead, he took hold of her ears, and then kicking the rope (still tied round his legs), the people above, with no small exultation, dragged them both out together.'" (Source: Frederick A. Ober, *"Old Put" the Patriot*)

‡**GENERAL [HORATIO] GATES**; "The general [Congress] now chose for the northern army, and upon whom they lavished all the support, both moral and material, which they had withheld from Schuyler, was **Horatio Gates**, 'the son of the housekeeper of the second Duke of Leeds.' Beyond his English birth and his somewhat remote connection with the English peerage, Gates had no claim whatever to command any army...it was given him solely because Congress, with colonial habits still strong upon them, were dazzled by the fact that he was an Englishman." (Source: Henry Cabot Lodge, *The Story of the Revolution*)

"An American army was organized at Hillsboro, North Carolina. Gates, the 'hero of Saratoga' was put in command by Congress, contrary to the wishes of **Washington**. The army moved forward and confronted **Cornwallis** at Camden. Here Gates met a crushing defeat, August 16, 1780,–the most overwhelming that had yet been given to an American army. In fact, his force was practically dispersed; but from its remnants and from fresh recruits, a new army was formed at Charlotte." (Source: E. G. Foster, *A History of the United States*)

‡**GENERAL [NATHANAEL] GREENE**; "For intellectual caliber [other officers in the American army] are dwarfed at once in comparison with Greene, who comes out at the end of the war with a military reputation scarcely, if at all, inferior to that of **Washington**. Nor was Greene less notable for the sweetness and purity of his character than for the scope of his intelligence. From lowly beginnings he had come to be, though still a young man, the most admired and respected citizen of Rhode Island. He had begun life as a blacksmith, but, inspired by an intense thirst for knowledge, he had soon become a learned blacksmith, well-versed in history, philosophy, and general literature. He had that rare genius which readily assimilates all kinds of knowledge through an inborn correctness of method. Whatever he touched, it was with a master hand, and his weight of sense soon won general recognition." (Source: John Fiske, *The American Revolution*)

Page 252

†**CANNONADE**, n. The act of discharging cannon and throwing balls, for the purpose of destroying an army, or battering a town, ship or fort. The term usually implies an attack of some continuance.

Page 253

†**SHEE'PISH**, a. Like a sheep; bashful; timorous to excess; over-modest; meanly diffident.

Page 254

‡**PETER OLIVER**; "Among the five occupants of the Bench in the superior Court of Massachusetts all save one were Loyalists; and three of them were driven into banishment. The political faith for which these gentlemen suffered is finely summarized in the epitaph on Chief Justice Oliver, the president of their tribunal, which may be seen in St. Philip's, Birmingham [England]; –a church standing in the very center of the city, with an ample space about it, and its doors hospitably open to the passing stranger...[A] monument is erected to the Honorable Peter Oliver, formerly His Majesty's Chief Justice of the Province of Massachusetts Bay in New England; and the inscription runs: 'In the year 1776, on a Dissolution of Government, He left his Native Country; but in all the consequent calamities his Magnanimity remained unshaken, and, (though the source of his misfortunes,) nothing could dissolve his Attachment to the British Government, nor lessen his love and loyalty to his Sovereign'...One of Oliver's colleagues died in Nova Scotia, and another in England; and at least five members of his family, who were living in Massachusetts as grown men before the Revolution broke out, are buried in different corners of our island [Great Britain]. When General De Lancey of New York was laid in his grave a fellow-refugee said, truly enough, that there would be scarcely a village in England without some American dust in it by the time they were all at rest." (Source: George Otto Trevelyan, *The American Revolution*, Part Two)

Page 255

†**SEDI''TIOUS**, a. [L. seditiosus.] Disposed to excite violent or irregular opposition to law or lawful authority; turbulent; factious, or guilty of sedition; as *seditious* citizens.

†**DEMAGOGUE**, n. Demagog. [Gr. The populas, and to lead.] 1. A leader of the people; an orator who pleases the populace and influences them to adhere to him.

Page 256

†**IM'PRECATE**, v.t. [L. imprecor; in and precor, to pray. See Pray.] To invoke, as an evil on any one; to pray that a curse or calamity may fall on one's self or on another person.

Page 257

†**DRAGOON**, n. [G., L, an ensign bearer; dragon; an appellation given to horsemen, perhaps for their rapidity or fierceness.] A soldier or musketeer who serves on horseback or on foot, as occasion may require. Their arms are a sword, a musket and a bayonet.

‡**SIR WILLIAM HOWE**; "It has been said, that we could not have chosen a better adversary than General Howe; and it is not improbable that one more enterprising and less methodical, might have pushed us harder: Yet, though he was indolent,

often treated us with unnecessary respect; and, in a too great security of his prey, might have meant to play us, as an angler plays a fish upon his hook, I am still inclined to think, that when he acted, he fought his army to advantage; that his dispositions were good, and planned with much discretion." (Source: Alexander Graydon, *Memoirs of His Own Time: With Reminiscences of the Men and Events of the Revolution*)

†**SCAB'BARD**, n. The sheath of a sword.

Page 260

†**EP'ITAPH**, n. [Gr. a sepulcher.] 1. An inscription on a monument, in honor or memory of the dead. 2. An eulogy, in prose or verse, composed without any intent to be engraven on a monument, as that on Alexander: *"Sufficit huic tumulus, cui non sufficeret orbis."*

‡**LIBERTY TREE**; "**Lafayette** said, when in Boston, 'The world should never forget the spot where once stood Liberty Tree, so famous in your annals.'...In August, 1775, the name of Liberty having become offensive to the Tories and their British allies, the tree was cut down by a party led by one Job Williams. 'Armed with axes, they made a furious attack upon it. After a long spell of laughing and grinning, sweating, swearing, and foaming, with malice diabolical, they cut down a tree because it bore the name of Liberty.' [*Essex Gazette*, 1775] Some idea of the size of the tree may be formed from the fact that it made fourteen cords of wood. The jesting at the expense of the Sons of Liberty had a sorry conclusion; one of the soldiers, in attempting to remove a limb, fell to the pavement and was killed." (Source: Samuel Adams Drake, *Old Landmarks and Historic Personages of Boston*)

Page 261

†**ANATH'EMA**, n. [Gr. to place behind, backward or at a distance, to separate.] Excommunication with curses. Hence, a curse or denunciation by ecclesiastical authority, accompanying excommunication. This species of excommunication was practiced in the ancient churches, against notorious offenders; all churches were warned not to receive them; all magistrates and private persons were admonished not to harbor or maintain them, and priests were enjoined not to converse with them, or attend their funeral.

†**BENEDIC'TION**, n. [L. benedictio, from bene, well, and dictio, speaking. See Boon and Diction.] 1. The act of blessing; a giving praise to God or rendering thanks for his favors; a blessing pronounced; hence grace before and after meals. 2. Blessing, prayer, or kind wishes, uttered in favor of any person or thing; a solemn or affectionate invocation of happiness; thanks; expression of gratitude.

Page 262

‡**SPARKS**; Historian Jared Sparks, author of the 12 volume *Life and Writings of George Washington* and the two volume *Life of George Washington*.

‡**LONGFELLOW, HENRY WORDSWORTH** (1807-1882); American poet, author of many works, including **"Evangeline"** and the collection *Voices of the Night*.

Page 263

†**MATCH'LOCK**, n. Formerly, the lock of a musket which was fired by a match.

‡**MR. PIERCE**; "William Pierce...The old gentleman will be ninety-one years of age next Christmas day [1835] , but still retains his faculties in remarkable vigor, and continues even in the active duties of the business, (at his shop in Marshall Street,)

which he has now followed, man and boy, for about seventy-six or seven years! He served his time with one John Adams, in Dock Square, where the sign of the great Boot now hangs, and opened shop for himself some years before the Revolution. He deserves at least, we surmise, the distinction of the oldest acting barber alive." (Source: Benjamin Bussey Thatcher, *Traits of the Tea Party: Being a Memoir of George R.T. Hewes, One of the Last of Its Survivors*)

Page 264

‡**DR. [CHARLES] CHAUNCEY**; "Dr. Chauncey [was the] minister of the First Church sixty years (1727-1787). Dr. Chauncey made a profound impression upon the literature and life of New England. Sixty or more of his sermons, –a few of them extended into volumes, –remain. He was devout, learned, and much inclined to controversy. His style was severely plain. He hated affectation; emotional religion did not interest him; enthusiasm excited his suspicion. He wrote and published much against Whitefield and the revivalists. Later in his ministry, he resisted by argument and appeal the introduction of bishops into the colonies by the British government. The exciting controversy over the introduction of the bishops in the time of **Governor Shute**, enlisted the best minds in the province, and gave a marked impulse to the literary spirit." (Source: Justin Winsor, *The Memorial History of Boston: including Suffolk County, Massachusetts*)

†**POMA'TUM**, v.t. To apply pomatum to the hair.

POMA'TUM, n. An unguent or composition used in dressing the hair. It is also used in medicine.

†**PRIVATEE'R**, n. [from private.] A ship or vessel of war owned and equipped by a private man or by individuals, at their own expense, to seize or plunder the ships of an enemy in war. Such a ship must be licensed or commissioned by government, or it is a pirate.

Page 267

‡**GENERAL [RICHARD] MONTGOMERY**; "The newspapers announce the most painful intelligence from our army in Canada. General Montgomery, the commander, made a desperate, but unsuccessful assault on the city of Quebec, on the 31st [December]. The event has proved most fatal and disastrous. General Montgomery, and his aid-de-camp, with several other officers, were slain. Colonel [Benedict] Arnold, the second in command, heroically passed the first barrier with his small party, and received a wound in his leg. About three hundred of the continental troops were made prisoners, and about sixty killed and wounded. We remain unacquainted with further particulars. The death of General Montgomery is universally deplored. In the public papers we have the following account of this brave officer: 'He was a captain of grenadiers in the 17th regiment of British troops, of which General Monckton was colonel. He served the last war in the expeditions in the West Indies and America, and returned with his regiment to England. In 1772 he quitted his regiment, through in a fair way of preferment. Whilst in America he imbibed an affection for this country–he had, while in the king's service, declared his disapprobation of the sentiments of the ministry, and viewed America as the rising seat of arts and freedom.'" (Source: James Thacher, *A Military Journal During the American Revolutionary War*)

†**ACQUIESCE**, v.i. acquiess'. [L. acquiesco, of ad and quiesco, to be quiet; quies, rest.] 1. To rest satisfied, or apparently satisfied, or to rest without opposition and discontent; usually implying previous opposition, uneasiness, or dislike, but ultimate compliance, or submission; as, to *acquiesce* in the dispensations of providence. 2. To assent to, upon conviction; as, to *acquiesce* in an opinion; that is, to

rest satisfied of its correctness, or propriety.

‡**SURRENDER AT SARATOGA**; "**[General John] Burgoyne**, deserted by his allies, his army half gone, with less than five days' food, with no word from Clinton, with no chance of escape, prepared honorably to surrender...At nine o'clock [in] the morning...he signed the convention. At eleven o'clock his troops marched to...the site of old Fort Hardy, and with tears coursing down bearded cheeks, with passionate sobs and oaths of rage and defiance, the soldiers kissing their guns with the tenderness of lovers, or with sudden frenzy knocking off the butts of their muskets, the drummers stamping on their drums, the king's army laid down their arms. No American eyes, except those of Morgan Lewis and James Wilkinson, aides of **General Gates**, beheld the surrender. As the British troops filed afterwards between the American lines, they saw no sign of exultation, but they heard the drums and fifes playing 'Yankee Doodle.' A few minutes later, Burgoyne and his suite rode to the headquarters of Gates. The English general, as if for a court holiday, glittered in scarlet and gold; Gates plainly clad in a blue overcoat, attended by General Schuyler in citizen's dress, who had come to congratulate him, and by his proud and happy staff, received his guest with urbane courtesy. They exchanged the compliments of soldiers. 'The fortune of war, General Gates, has made me your prisoner.' Gates gracefully replied, 'I shall always be ready to testify that it has not been through any fault of your Excellency.' The generals entered the tent of Gates and dined together. With the same courtly compliment the English general toasted **General Washington**, the American general toasted the king. Then, as the English army, without artillery or arms, approached on their march to the sea, the two generals stepped out in front of the tent, and standing together conspicuous upon this spot, in full view of the Americans and of the British army, General Burgoyne drew his sword, bowed, and presented it to General Gates. General Gates bowed, received the sword, and returned it to General Burgoyne. Such was the simple ceremony that marked the turning point of the **Revolution**." (Source: William L. Stone, *Memoir of the Centennial Celebration of Burgoyne's Surrender*)

Page 268

†**ADVERT'**, v.i. [L. adverto, of ad and verto, to turn.] To turn the mind or attention to; to regard, observe, or notice: with to; as, he *adverted* to what was said, or to a circumstance that occurred.

Page 269

‡**SURRENDER AT YORKTOWN, VIRGINIA**; "**General Cornwallis** thus narrates the circumstances of his capitulation at Yorktown in 1781.

YORKTOWN, VIRGINIA, OCT. 20, 1781

> 'I have the mortification to inform your Excellency that I have been forced to give up the posts of York and Gloucester, and to surrender the troops under my command, by capitulation, on the 19th instant, as prisoners of war to the combined forces of America and France...Our numbers had been diminished by the enemy's fire, but particularly by sickness, and the strength and spirits of those in the works were much exhausted by the fatigue of constant watching and unremitting duty. Under all these circumstances, I thought it would have been wanton and inhuman to the last degree to sacrifice the lives of this small body of gallant soldiers, who had ever behaved with so much fidelity and courage, by exposing them to an assault which, from the numbers and precautions of the enemy, could not fail to succeed. I therefore proposed to capitulate; and I have the honor to enclose to your Excellency the copy of the correspondence between General Washington and me on that subject, and the terms of capitulation agreed upon. I sincerely lament that better could not be obtained, but I have neglected nothing in my power to alleviate the misfortune and distress of both officers and soldiers...The treatment, in general, that we have received from the enemy

since our surrender has been perfectly good and proper, but the kindness and attention that has been shown to us by the French officers in particular–their delicate sensibility of our situation, their generous and pressing offer of money, both public and private, to any amount–has really gone beyond what I can possibly describe, and will, I hope, make an impression on the breast of every British officer, whenever the fortune of war should put any of them into our power.'"

(Source: James Harvey Robinson and Charles Austin Beard, *Readings in Modern European History*)

Page 270

†**MIEN**, n. Look; air; manner; external appearance; carriage; as a lofty *mien*; a majestic *mien*.

‡**SHAY'S WAR**; Crushing debt, and economic and political uncertainty after the Revolutionary War, created social unrest. "...**Daniel Shays**, a captain resigned from the Revolutionary army, brave in the field but unfit for a general, bankrupt in fortune, came to the front in western Massachusetts. Luke Day, another captain, major by brevet for honorable service, a stronger man, was 'the master spirit of the insurrection;' but Shays was the more prominent leader. The epidemic spread from Hampshire to Worcester, to Middlesex and Essex. Recruits were drilled by the leaders about Springfield, and those who were able armed themselves. Judges were threatened and the courts interrupted; the legislature, in the lower house at least, was infected. But the spirit of order gradually prevailed, more severe laws against illegal assemblies and rioting were passed, *habeas corpus* was suspended for eight months, and taxation was somewhat ameliorated.

"In January, 1787, the rebellion culminated. Some 1,800 men were organized in or near Springfield to resist the authority of the commonwealth. The state troops were mustered under the command of **Major General Lincoln**, who moved vigorously against the insurgents. The rebellion crumbled at the first shock, and there was little or no blood shed. The state treated the misguided rebels with great clemency.

"This rebellion was the sore which revealed disease in the whole body politic..." (Source: William Babcock Weeden, *Economic and Social History of New England, 1620-1789*)

Page 271

‡**JAMES BOWDOIN**; "The council, purged by dropping **Hutchinson** and several other officials, was now chiefly influenced by James Bowdoin. His grandfather, a French Huguenot, had migrated to New England shortly after the revocation of the Edict of Nantes. His father, from very small beginnings, had acquired the largest fortune in Boston, the most of which, Bowdoin, an only son, had inherited at the age of twenty-one. In the prime of life, of elevated character and a studious turn of mind, for several years past a member of the council, he acted in close concert with **[Samuel] Adams**, to whose impetuous ardor and restless activity his less excitable but not less firm temper served as a useful counterpoise." (Source: Richard Hildreth, *The History of the United States of America*)

Page 272

‡**SAMUEL ADAMS**; "Samuel Adams was a stern Puritan, a true representative of the founders of Massachusetts, from his early youth a warm politician and ardent opposer of prerogative, but till recently without much influence. Educated at Cambridge and intended for the ministry, circumstances had forced him to adopt his father's business of a merchant. Not succeeding in that, he had accepted the office

of collector of town taxes; but some deficiency in his accounts–for he was no man of business–threw him into the shade. The recent troubles had brought him conspicuously forward. His energy and courage made him leader in the Boston town meetings. Chosen in Thacher's place as one of the representatives, he accepted the office of clerk of the House–a place which not only gave him a small income, but also enabled him to exercise a certain influence over the course of proceeding. While he devoted himself to politics, it was chiefly the industry of his wife that supported the family. But, though poor, Adams was incorruptible. It had been suggested to quiet him with a government place; but **Hutchinson** declared that such was his 'obstinacy and inflexible disposition,' that no gift nor office could ever conciliate him." (Source: Richard Hildreth, The History of the United States of America)

Page 274

†**PON'DEROUS**, a. [L. ponderosus.] Very heavy; weighty; as a *ponderous* shield; a *ponderous* load.

Page 275

†**HUZZ'A**, n. A shout of joy; a foreign word used in writing only, and most preposterously, as it is never used in practice. The word used in our native word hoora, or hoorah.

†**CAPER**, v.i. To leap; to skip or jump; to prance; to spring.

Page 276

†**COLLOQUY**, n. Conversation; mutual discourse of two or more; conference; dialogue.

‡**SIR RICHARD SALTONSTALL**; "Sir Richard Saltonstall...early engaged in the New England enterprise, and in the charter of Charles I is the first named associate to the six original patentees of Massachusetts Bay, and was appointed the first assistant. On board the *Arbella*, at Yarmouth, he, with **Gov. Winthrop** and others, signed that 'humble request of his Majesty's loyal subjects the governor and company late gone for New England to the rest of their brethren in and of the church of England,' in which they take so affecting a leave of their native land on their departure for their 'poor cottages in the wilderness.' He arrived at Salem, in the *Arbella*, June 12th, 1630...The sufferings of those who engaged in this new settlement in the wilderness were extreme the first winter, and Sir Richard Saltonstall became discouraged from remaining himself, but left his two eldest sons...

"Sir Richard Saltonstall always continued to be the friend of the colony and was actively engaged in their behalf...[He] was a man of singular liberality in religion, for a Puritan of the age in which he lived, and was offended at the bigotry of his associates, who were no sooner secure from persecution themselves, than they began to persecute in their turn." (Source: *Collections of the Massachusetts Historical Society*)

Page 277

‡**HUGH PETERS**; "The immediate effects of the restoration [of the monarchy in England] were saddened by the bitterness of revenge. All the **regicides** that were seized would have perished, but for Charles II, whom good nature led at last to exclaim, "I am tired of hanging, except for new offenses." All haste was, however, made to dispatch half a score of victims, as if to appease the shade of **Charles I** [executed by Parliament under **Oliver Cromwell**]; and among the selected victims was Hugh Peters, once the minister of Salem, the father-in-law of the younger Winthrop; one

whom **Roger Williams** honored and loved, and whom Milton is supposed to include among

Men whose life, learning, faith, and pure intent,
Would have been held in high esteem with Paul.

"As a preacher, his homely energy resembled the eloquence of Latimer and earlier divines; in Salem he won the general affection; he was ever zealous to advance the interests and quicken the industry of New England, and had assisted in founding the earliest college. His was the fanaticism of an ill-balanced mind, mastered by great ideas, which it imperfectly comprehends; and therefore he repelled monarchy and Episcopacy with excited passion. Though he was not himself a regicide, his zeal made him virtually an accomplice, by his influence over others. He could not consider consequences, and zeal overwhelmed his judgment. Nor was he entirely free from that bigotry which refuses to extend the rights of humanity beyond its own altars; he could thank God for the massacres of Cromwell in Ireland. And yet benevolence was deeply fixed in his heart; he ever advocated the rights of the feeble, and pleaded for the sufferings of the poor. Of his whole career it was said, that 'many godly in New England dared not condemn what Hugh Peters had done.' His arraignment, his trial, and his execution, were scenes of wanton injustice. He was allowed no counsel; and, indeed, his death had been resolved upon beforehand, though even false witnesses did not substantiate the specific charges urged against him. His last thoughts reverted to Massachusetts. 'Go home to New England, and trust God there;' it was his final counsel to his daughter. At the gallows, to which he was brought on the fourteenth day of October, 1666, he was compelled to wait while the body of his friend Cooke, who had just been hanged, was cut down and quartered before his eyes. 'How do you like this?' cried executioner, rubbing his bloody hands. 'I thank God,' replied the martyr, 'I am not terrified at it; you may do your worst.' To his friends he said, 'Weep not for me; my heart is full of comfort;' and he smiled as he made himself ready to leave the world. Even death could not save him from his enemies; the bias of party corrupts the judgments, and cruelty justified itself by defaming its victim. So perished a freeman of Massachusetts–the first who lost his life for opposition to monarchy. The blood of Massachusetts was destined to flow freely on the field of battle for the same cause; the streams were first opened beneath the gallows." (Source: George Bancroft, *History of the Colonization of the United States*)

†**REG'ICIDE**, n. [L. rex, king, and caedo, to slay.] A king-killer; one who murders a king.

‡**WHALLEY, GOFFE, AND DIXWELL**; "Of the judges [**regicides**] of **King Charles I**, three escaped to America. Edward Whalley–who had first won laurels in the field of Naseby, had ever enjoyed the confidence of **Cromwell**, and remained to the last an enemy to the Stuarts, and a friend to the interests of the Independents–and William Goffe–a firm friend to the family of Cromwell, a good soldier, and an ardent partisan, but ignorant of the true principles of freedom–arrived in Boston, where **Endicot**, the governor, received them with courtesy. For nearly a year, they resided unmolested within the limits of Massachusetts, holding meetings in every house, where they preached and prayed, and gained universal applause. When warrants arrived from England for their apprehension, they, in 1661, fled across the country to New Haven, where it was esteemed a crime against God to betray the wanderer or give up the outcast. Yet such diligent search was made for them, that they never were in security...John Dixwell, more fortunate, was able to live undiscovered. Changing his name, and becoming absorbed among the inhabitants of New Haven, he married, and lived peacefully and happily." (Source: George Bancroft, *History of the Colonization of the United States*)

Grandfather's Chair

Page 278

†**CAPACIOUS**, a. 1. Wide; large; that will hold much; as a *capacious* vessel. 2. Broad; extensive; as a *capacious* bay or harbor. 3. Extensive; comprehensive; able to take a wide view; as a *capacious* mind.

†**ORAC'ULAR, ORAC'ULARLY, ORAC'ULOUS**, a. 1. Uttering oracles; as an *oracular* tongue. 2. Positive; authoritative; magisterial; as *oraculous* expressions of sentiments.

Page 280

†**RAB'BLE**, n. [L. rabula, a brawler, from rabo, to rave.] A tumultuous crowd of vulgar, noisy people; the mob; a confused disorderly crowd.

†**REPENT'**, v.t. To remember with sorrow; as, to *repent* rash words; to *repent* an injury done to a neighbor; to *repent* follies and vices.

Page 281

†**WAINSCOT**, n. In building, timber-work serving to line the walls of a room, being made in panels.

†**LANT'HORN**, n. In architecture, a little dome raised over the roof of a building to give light, and to serve as a crowning to the fabric.

†**PLATE**, n. [L. Latus, with the radical sense of laid, spread.] A piece of wrought silver, as a dish or other shallow vessel; hence, vessels of silver; wrought silver in general. Plate, by the laws of some states, is subject to a tax by the ounce.

†**CAMLET**, n. A stuff originally made of camels hair. It is now made, sometimes of wool, sometimes of silk, sometimes of hair, especially that of goats, with wool or silk. In some, the warp is silk and wool twisted together, and the woof is hair. The pure oriental camlet is made solely from the hair of a sort of goat, Angora. Camlets are now made in Europe.

†**SURTOUT**, n. A man's coat to be worn over his other garments.

Page 282

†**DETESTATION**, n. Extreme hatred; abhorrence; with *of*. The good man entertains uniformly a *detestation* of sin.

†**CONCESSION**, n. [L. From concedo. See Concede.] The act of granting or yielding; usually implying a demand, claim, or request from the party to whom it is made, and thus distinguished from giving, which is voluntary or spontaneous.

Index

A

B

C

Q

R

Y

Printed in the United States
102595LV00004B/112/A

9 780979 296802